MW00668638

NFPA 70E®

Standard for

Electrical Safety in the Workplace®

2021 Edition

This edition of *NFPA 70E®*, *Standard for Electrical Safety in the Workplace®*, was prepared by the Technical Committee on Electrical Safety in the Workplace and released by the Correlating Committee on National Electrical Code®. It was issued by the Standards Council on June 1, 2020, with an effective date of June 21, 2020, and supersedes all previous editions.

This edition of *NFPA 70E* was approved as an American National Standard on June 21, 2020.

Foreword to *NFPA 70E*

The Standards Council of the National Fire Protection Association announced the formal appointment of a new electrical standards development committee on January 7, 1976. The Committee on Electrical Safety Requirements for Employee Workplaces reported to the association through the Technical Correlating Committee on *National Electrical Code®* (*NEC®*). The committee was formed to assist OSHA in preparing an electrical safety standard that would serve OSHA's needs and that could be expeditiously promulgated through the provisions of Section 6(b) of the Occupational Safety and Health Act. OSHA found that in attempting to utilize the latest edition of the *NEC*, it was confronted with the following problems:

(1) OSHA could only adopt or modify a standard through procedures that provide for public notice, opportunity for public comment, and public hearings. The adoption of a new *NEC* edition by these procedures would require extensive effort and application of resources by OSHA and others. Going through the procedures might result in requirements substantially different from those of the *NEC*, thereby creating a conflict between the two standards.

(2) The *NEC* is intended for use primarily by those who design, install, and inspect electrical installations. Most of the *NEC* requirements are not electrical safety–related work practices, electrical system maintenance, or directly related to employee safety. However, OSHA electrical regulations, which address employers and employees in their workplaces, needed to consider and develop these safety areas.

It became apparent that a need existed for a new standard tailored to fulfill OSHA's responsibilities that would still be fully consistent with the *NEC*. This led to the concept of a new document that would extract suitable portions from the *NEC* and from other documents applicable to electrical safety. This concept and an offer of assistance was submitted in May 1975 to the Assistant Secretary of Labor for OSHA, who responded as follows: "The concept, procedures, and scope of the effort discussed with my staff for preparing the subject standard appear to have great merit, and an apparent need exists for this proposed consensus document which OSHA could consider for promulgation under the provisions of Section 6(b) of the Act. OSHA does have an interest in this effort and believes the proposed standard would serve a useful purpose." With this positive encouragement from OSHA, the NFPA Electrical Section unanimously supported a recommendation that the *NEC* Correlating Committee examine the feasibility of developing a document for evaluating electrical safety in the workplace. With recommendations from the Electrical Section and Correlating Committee, the Standards Council authorized the establishment of a committee to carry out this examination.

The committee would develop a standard for electrical installations that would be compatible with the OSHA requirements for employee safety in locations covered by the *NEC*. The standard was visualized as consisting of four major parts: Part I, Installation Safety Requirements; Part II, Safety-Related Work Practices; Part III, Safety-Related Maintenance Requirements; and Part IV, Safety Requirements for Special Equipment. It was not considered essential for all of the parts to be completed before the standard was published and made available. Each part was recognized as being an important aspect of electrical safety in the workplace, but the parts were sufficiently independent of each other to permit their separate publication. The first edition of NFPA *70E, Standard for Electrical Safety Requirements for Employee Workplaces*, was published in 1979 and included only Part I, Installation Safety Requirements.

The second edition published in 1981 included a new Part II, Safety-Related Work Practices. In 1983, the third edition added a new Part III, Safety-Related Maintenance Requirements. In 1988, the fourth edition was published with only minor revisions.

The 1995 edition included major revisions to Part I to conform to the 1993 edition of the *NEC*. The concepts of "limits of approach" and establishment of an "arc" were introduced in Part II. In 2000, the sixth edition included an update of Part I to the 1999 *NEC*, as well as a new Part IV, Safety Requirements for Special Equipment. Part II continued to focus on establishing flash protection boundaries and the use of personal protective equipment (PPE). Also, charts were added to Part II to assist in applying appropriate protective clothing and personal protective equipment for common tasks.

The 2004 edition presented several significant changes. The major changes emphasized safe work practices. Clarity and usability of the document were also enhanced. The title was changed to *Standard for Electrical Safety in the Workplace*. The document was reformatted to comply with the *National Electrical Code Style Manual*. The existing parts were renamed as chapters and were reorganized with the safety-related work practices relocated to the front of the document to highlight the emphasis, followed by safety-related maintenance requirements, safety requirements for special equipment, and safety-related installation requirements. The chapter on safety-related work practices also was reorganized to emphasize that working on live parts is the last alternative work practice. An energized electrical work permit and related requirements were incorporated into the document.

This standard is compatible with the *NEC* but is not intended to be used, nor can it be used, in lieu of the *NEC*. Chapter 4, Specific Purpose Equipment and Installations, was intended to serve a very specific need of OSHA. It was not intended to be applied as a design, installation, modification, or construction standard for an electrical installation or system. Its content was intentionally limited in comparison to the *NEC* in order to apply to an electrical installation or a system as part of an employee's workplace. Chapter 4 was updated to correlate with the 2002 edition of the *NEC*, but requirements not directly associated with employee safety were not included. Omission of *NEC* requirements did not affect the *NEC*, nor were omitted requirements considered as unimportant. They are essential to the *NEC* and its intended application — that is, its use by those who design, install, and inspect electrical installations. NFPA *70E*, on the other hand, is intended for use by employers, employees, and OSHA.

Requirements were upgraded throughout the 2009 edition. Chapter 4 was deleted because it was a duplicate of *NEC* installation requirements. Article 350 was added for R&D facilities. Other changes included significant revisions to Annex D, Annex F, and Annex J and the addition of Annex M, Annex N, and Annex O.

The 2012 edition marked another waypoint as this standard continued to evolve to meet the electrical safety needs of employers and employees. New research, new technology, and technical input from users provided the foundation for new and revised requirements that addressed the electrical hazards encountered by employees in current workplaces. Expanded or clarified requirements, inclusion of technical material not previously covered, and removal of requirements related to the safe installation of electrical equipment rather than being safe electrical work practices were some of the major actions undertaken during the revision cycle. In addition, requirements covering the separate but directly related concepts of hazard identification and risk assessment were revised to clarify the concepts. A significant revision to Annex F provided extensive coverage of this topic to assist users with implementing effective hazard identification and risk assessment procedures. Annex P on aligning NFPA *70E* implementation with occupational health and safety management standards was added.

The majority of changes occurred in Chapter 1. Article 105, Application of Safety-Related Work Practices, and a requirement for hearing protection when working within an arc flash boundary were added, as were work practice requirements on the use of GFCIs to protect employees. Clarification was made that Article 130 applies whether incident energy analysis or the hazard/risk table was used to determine use and level of PPE. Short-circuit current, fault clearing time, and arc flash boundary information were included in the hazard/risk category tables. Another major revision included changing "flame-resistant (FR)" to "arc-rated (AR)" in regard to PPE.

The 2015 edition incorporated a major shift in how stakeholders evaluate electrical risk. In support of this, new definitions for *hazard, hazardous, risk,* and *risk assessment* were added to Article 100. Throughout the document, changes were made to provide clarity to users, such as changing *hazard analysis* to *risk assessment*. These global changes ensured consistent use of these terms throughout the document and provided consistency between *NFPA 70E* and other standards that address hazards and risk. Other major revisions included the following:

(1) The definition of a qualified person was revised to correlate with the OSHA definition.

(2) Safety-related maintenance requirements and other administrative controls were added to the scope statement to clarify that training and auditing are equally important safety-related work practices.

(3) An electrical safety program must consider condition of maintenance.

(4) Clarification was provided that the equipment owner or the owner's designated representative is responsible for maintenance of the electrical equipment and documentation.

(5) New maintenance requirements were added for test instruments and associated test leads utilized in the verification of the absence or presence of voltages.

(6) New requirements clarified where normal operation of electric equipment is permitted.

(7) Clarification was made that either the incident energy analysis method or arc flash PPE category method can be used on a piece of equipment for the selection of PPE, but not both. The revision clarified that the results of an incident energy analysis is not permitted to be used to specify an arc flash PPE category.

(8) A new task-based table combined the previously separate ac and dc tables used to determine when arc flash PPE is required and made them consistent, improving usability.

(9) New equipment-based tables were added for determining the arc flash PPE category for ac systems and for dc systems.

(10) Hazard/risk category 0 was removed because the new PPE table only specifies PPE for work within the arc flash boundary. Hazard/risk category was also changed to PPE category.

(11) Prohibited approach boundary was deleted because additional protective equipment was not required when crossing this boundary.

(12) The criterion to use insulated tools or handling equipment was changed from the limited approach boundary to restricted approach boundary.

(13) All references to bare-hand work were removed. This work is considered to be a "utility type" line work technique more appropriately addressed in other standards.

(14) Field-marked equipment labeling requirements were revised to require an updated label when the arc flash hazard risk assessment identifies a change that renders the label inaccurate.

(15) A risk assessment is required prior to any work on a battery system to identify the chemical, electrical shock, and arc flash hazards and assess the risks associated with the type of tasks to be performed.

The 2018 edition continued to evolve to address risk assessment and introduce human factors, such as human error, as part of that assessment. Annex Q, Human Performance and Workplace Electrical Safety, was included to provide guidance in this area. This edition emphasized the need to use the hierarchy of risk controls by moving it from an informational note into the text of the standard. *NFPA 70E* explicitly stated that the first priority must be the elimination of the hazard.

The previous arc flash hazard identification table [Table 130.7(C)(15)(A)(a)] was modified to determine the likelihood that an arc flash could occur and renumbered as Table 130.5(C). This modified table could be used with either method of arc flash risk assessment.

The most notable change for the 2018 edition was that tables and text that specified PPE standards were moved to informational tables or notes. In previous editions employers were, and still are, required to verify that appropriate PPE is given to employees. Section 130.7(C)(14)(b) was added to provide guidance on conformity assessment of PPE. These changes did not alter the employer's responsibility for determining the validity of the PPE manufacturer's claims.

Definitions for *fault current* and *available fault current* were added, and other terms used throughout the standard for this current were changed for consistency. Article 120 was rearranged to present the requirements for establishing an electrically safe work condition in a logical order of application of the program. Article 320 introduced voltage thresholds of 50 Vac and 100 Vdc specifically for batteries and battery rooms to address the unique situations in these locations. Article 330 addressing lasers was extensively revised to address safety-related maintenance issues rather than issues associated with laser use. Article 350 introduced an Electrical Safety Authority as a possible authority having jurisdiction for laboratories.

For the 2021 edition, Article 110 was revised to incorporate the general requirements for electrical safety-related work programs, practices, and procedures from other articles. The reference to arc-resistant switchgear has been changed to arc-resistant equipment in Tables 130.5(C) and 130.7(C)(15)(a) to address the use of other types of arc-resistant equipment. Article 360, Safety-Related Requirements for Capacitors, and Annex R, Working with Capacitors, were added to address specific electrical safety requirements unique to capacitors. Annex D, Incident Energy and Arc Flash Boundary Calculation Methods, was revised to reference IEEE-1584-2018 as a method of calculation.

Contents

Correlating Committee on National Electrical Code®

Lawrence S. Ayer, *Chair*
Biz Com Electric, Inc., OH [IM]
Rep. Independent Electrical Contractors, Inc.

James E. Brunssen, Telcordia Technologies (Ericsson), NJ [UT]
    Rep. Alliance for Telecommunications Industry Solutions
Kevin L. Dressman, US Department of Energy, MD [U]
Palmer L. Hickman, Electrical Training Alliance, MD [L]
    Rep. International Brotherhood of Electrical Workers
Richard A. Holub, The DuPont Company, Inc., DE [U]
    Rep. American Chemistry Council
Michael J. Johnston, National Electrical Contractors Association, MD [IM]

John R. Kovacik, UL LLC, IL [RT]
Alan Manche, Schneider Electric, KY [M]
Roger D. McDaniel, Georgia Power Company, GA [UT]
    Rep. Electric Light & Power Group/EEI
George A. Straniero, AFC Cable Systems, Inc., NJ [M]
    Rep. National Electrical Manufacturers Association
David A. Williams, Delta Charter Township, MI [E]
    Rep. International Association of Electrical Inspectors

Alternates

Roland E. Deike, Jr., CenterPoint Energy, Inc., TX [UT]
    (Alt. to Roger D. McDaniel)
James T. Dollard, Jr., IBEW Local Union 98, PA [L]
    (Alt. to Palmer L. Hickman)
Ernest J. Gallo, Telcordia Technologies (Ericsson), NJ [UT]
    (Alt. to James E. Brunssen)
David L. Hittinger, Independent Electrical Contractors of Greater Cincinnati, OH [IM]
    (Alt. to Lawrence S. Ayer)
David H. Kendall, ABB Inc., TN [M]
    (Alt. to George A. Straniero)

Robert A. McCullough, Tuckerton, NJ [E]
    (Alt. to David A. Williams)
Robert D. Osborne, UL LLC, NC [RT]
    (Alt. to John R. Kovacik)
Christine T. Porter, Intertek Testing Services, WA [RT]
    (Voting Alt.)
Timothy James Schultheis, T.S.B Inc., Schultheis Electric, PA [IM]
    (Alt. to Michael J. Johnston)

Nonvoting

Timothy J. Pope, Canadian Standards Association, Canada [SE]
    Rep. CSA/Canadian Electrical Code Committee
William R. Drake, Fairfield, CA [M]
    (Member Emeritus)

Jeffrey S. Sargent, NFPA Staff Liaison

D. Harold Ware, Libra Electric Company, OK [IM]
    (Member Emeritus)

This list represents the membership at the time the Committee was balloted on the final text of this edition. Since that time, changes in the membership may have occurred. A key to classifications is found at the back of the document.

NOTE: Membership on a committee shall not in and of itself constitute an endorsement of the Association or any document developed by the committee on which the member serves.

Committee Scope: This Committee shall have primary responsibility for documents on minimizing the risk of electricity as a source of electric shock and as a potential ignition source of fires and explosions. It shall also be responsible for text to minimize the propagation of fire and explosions due to electrical installations.

Technical Committee on Electrical Safety in the Workplace

Louis A. Barrios, *Chair*
Shell Global Solutions, TX [U]
Rep. American Petroleum Institute

Paul D. Barnhart, UL LLC, NC [RT]

William Bruce Bowman, Fox Systems, Inc., GA [IM]
Rep. Independent Electrical Contractors, Inc.

Steven C. Chybowski, Rockwell Automation Inc., WI [M]

Daryld Ray Crow, DRC Consulting, Ltd., UT [M]
Rep. The Aluminum Association, Inc.

Thomas B. Dyson, Ameren Services, MO [U]
Rep. Edison Electric Institute

Ernest J. Gallo, Telcordia Technologies (Ericsson), NJ [U]
Rep. Alliance for Telecommunications Industry Solutions

Bobby J. Gray, Hoydar/Buck, Inc., WA [E]

William R. Harris, General Motors Company, MI [U]

Palmer L. Hickman, Electrical Training Alliance, MD [L]
Rep. International Brotherhood of Electrical Workers

Mark R. Hilbert, MR Hilbert Electrical Inspections & Training, NH [E]
Rep. International Association of Electrical Inspectors

Kevin J. Lippert, Eaton Corporation, PA [M]
Rep. National Electrical Manufacturers Association

Terrance L. McKinch, Mortenson Construction, MI [U]

Mark McNellis, Sandia National Laboratories, NM [U]

Charles R. Miller, Lighthouse Educational Services, TN [SE]

Daleep C. Mohla, DCM Electrical Consulting Services, Inc., TX [SE]
Rep. Institute of Electrical & Electronics Engineers, Inc.

James K. Niemira, S&C Electric Company, IL [M]

Thomas D. Norwood, AVO Training Institute, TX [SE]

David A. Pace, Olin Corporation, AL [U]
Rep. American Chemistry Council

James G. Stallcup, Grayboy, Inc., TX [SE]

Charlie R. Thurmond III, ThyssenKrupp Elevator, TN [IM]
Rep. National Elevator Industry Inc.

John M. Tobias, US Department of the Army, MD [U]

Rodney J. West, Schneider Electric, OH [M]

James R. White, Shermco Industries, Inc., TX [IM]
Rep. InterNational Electrical Testing Association

Jason Wolf, The ESCO Group, IA [IM]
Rep. National Electrical Contractors Association

Alternates

Bill Alderton, Schneider Electric, OH [M]
(Alt. to Rodney J. West)

Lawrence S. Ayer, Biz Com Electric, Inc., OH [IM]
(Alt. to William Bruce Bowman)

James E. Brunssen, Telcordia Technologies (Ericsson), NJ [U]
(Alt. to Ernest J. Gallo)

Jeffrey Paul Conkwright, Mortenson Energy Services, MN [U]
(Alt. to Terrance L. McKinch)

Paul Dobrowsky, Innovative Technology Services, NY [SE]
(Alt. to Daleep C. Mohla)

James T. Dollard, Jr., IBEW Local Union 98, PA [L]
(Alt. to Palmer L. Hickman)

Heath Garrison, National Renewable Energy Laboratory, CO [U]
(Alt. to Mark McNellis)

Eric Glaude, Chevron, TX [U]
(Alt. to Louis A. Barrios)

Donald Charles Hacke, Kone Inc., IL [IM]
(Alt. to Charlie R. Thurmond III)

Martin Nagel, General Motors Company, MI [U]
(Alt. to William R. Harris)

Larry D. Perkins, US Department of Energy, TN [E]
(Alt. to Bobby J. Gray)

Jim Phillips, Brainfiller, Inc., AZ [SE]
(Alt. to Charles R. Miller)

Roy K. Sparks, III, Eli Lilly and Company, IN [U]
(Alt. to David A. Pace)

Gregory J. Steinman, Thomas & Betts Corporation, TN [M]
(Alt. to Kevin J. Lippert)

Samuel B. Stonerock, Southern California Edison Company, CA [SE]
(Voting Alt.)

Wesley L. Wheeler, National Electrical Contractors Association, MD [IM]
(Alt. to Jason Wolf)

Ron Widup, Shermco Industries, TX [IM]
(Alt. to James R. White)

Nonvoting

Carolyn Black, Mount Vernon Mills, Canada [SE]
Rep. Canadian Standards Association

Mike Doherty, Blue Arc Electrical Safety Technologies, Inc., Canada [SE]
Rep. Canadian Standards Association

David M. Wallis, Consultant, MD [SE]
(Member Emeritus)

Christopher Coache, NFPA Staff Liaison

This list represents the membership at the time the Committee was balloted on the final text of this edition. Since that time, changes in the membership may have occurred. A key to classifications is found at the back of the document.

NOTE: Membership on a committee shall not in and of itself constitute an endorsement of the Association or any document developed by the committee on which the member serves.

Committee Scope: This Committee shall have primary responsibility for documents for work practices that are necessary to provide a practical safe workplace relative to the hazards associated with electrical energy. This Committee shall have primary jurisdiction, but shall report to Correlating Committee of the National Electrical Code.

NFPA 70E

Electrical Safety in the Workplace

2021 Edition

IMPORTANT NOTE: This NFPA document is made available for use subject to important notices and legal disclaimers. These notices and disclaimers appear in all publications containing this document and may be found under the heading "Important Notices and Disclaimers Concerning NFPA Documents." They can also be viewed at www.nfpa.org/disclaimers or obtained on request from NFPA.

UPDATES, ALERTS, AND FUTURE EDITIONS: New editions of NFPA codes, standards, recommended practices, and guides (i.e., NFPA Standards) are released on scheduled revision cycles. This edition may be superseded by a later one, or it may be amended outside of its scheduled revision cycle through the issuance of Tentative Interim Amendments (TIAs). An official NFPA Standard at any point in time consists of the current edition of the document, together with all TIAs and Errata in effect. To verify that this document is the current edition or to determine if it has been amended by TIAs or Errata, please consult the National Fire Codes® Subscription Service or the "List of NFPA Codes & Standards" at www.nfpa.org/docinfo. In addition to TIAs and Errata, the document information pages also include the option to sign up for alerts for individual documents and to be involved in the development of the next edition.

A reference in brackets [ ] following a section or paragraph indicates material that has been extracted from another NFPA document. Extracted text may be edited for consistency and style and may include the revision of internal paragraph references and other references as appropriate. Requests for interpretations or revisions of extracted text shall be sent to the technical committee responsible for the source document.

Information on referenced and extracted publications can be found in Informative Annex A.

ARTICLE 90
Introduction

90.1 Purpose. The purpose of this standard is to provide a practical safe working area for employees relative to the hazards arising from the use of electricity.

90.2 Scope.

(A) Covered. This standard addresses electrical safety-related work practices, safety-related maintenance requirements, and other administrative controls for employee workplaces that are necessary for the practical safeguarding of employees relative to the hazards associated with electrical energy during activities such as the installation, removal, inspection, operation, maintenance, and demolition of electric conductors, electric equipment, signaling and communications conductors and equipment, and raceways. This standard also includes safe work practices for employees performing other work activities that can expose them to electrical hazards as well as safe work practices for the following:

(1) Installation of conductors and equipment that connect to the supply of electricity

(2) Installations used by the electric utility, such as office buildings, warehouses, garages, machine shops, and recreational buildings that are not an integral part of a generating plant, substation, or control center

Informational Note: This standard addresses safety of workers whose job responsibilities involve interaction with energized electrical equipment and systems with potential exposure to electrical hazards. Concepts in this standard are often adapted to other workers whose exposure to electrical hazards is unintentional or not recognized as part of their job responsibilities. The highest risk for injury from electrical hazards for other workers involve unintentional contact with overhead power lines and electric shock from machines, tools, and appliances.

(B) Not Covered. This standard does not cover safety-related work practices for the following:

(1) Installations in ships, watercraft other than floating buildings, railway rolling stock, aircraft, or automotive vehicles other than mobile homes and recreational vehicles

(2) Installations of railways for generation, transformation, transmission, or distribution of power used exclusively for operation of rolling stock or installations used exclusively for signaling and communications purposes

(3) Installations of communications equipment under the exclusive control of communications utilities located outdoors or in building spaces used exclusively for such installations

(4) Installations under the exclusive control of an electric utility where such installations:

a. Consist of service drops or service laterals, and associated metering, or

b. Are located in legally established easements or rights-of-way designated by or recognized by public service commissions, utility commissions, or other regulatory agencies having jurisdiction for such installations, or

c. Are on property owned or leased by the electric utility for the purpose of communications, metering, generation, control, transformation, transmission, or distribution of electric energy, or

d. Are located by other written agreements either designated by or recognized by public service commissions, utility commissions, or other regulatory agencies having jurisdiction for such installations. These written agreements shall be limited to installations for the purpose of communications, metering, generation, control, transformation, transmission, or distribution of electric energy where legally established easements or rights-of-way cannot be obtained. These installations shall be limited to federal lands, Native American reservations through the U.S. Department of the Interior Bureau of Indian Affairs, military bases, lands controlled by port authorities and state agencies and departments, and lands owned by railroads.

90.3 Standard Arrangement. This standard is divided into the introduction and three chapters, as shown in Figure 90.3. Chapter 1 applies generally, Chapter 2 addresses safety-related maintenance requirements, and Chapter 3 supplements or modifies Chapter 1 with safety requirements for special equipment.

Informative annexes are not part of the requirements of this standard but are included for informational purposes only.

90.4 Mandatory Rules, Permissive Rules, and Explanatory Material.

(A) Mandatory Rules. Mandatory rules of this standard are those that identify actions that are specifically required or prohibited and are characterized by the use of the terms *shall* or *shall not.*

(B) Permissive Rules. Permissive rules of this standard are those that identify actions that are allowed but not required, are normally used to describe options or alternative methods, and are characterized by the use of the terms *shall be permitted* or *shall not be required.*

(C) Explanatory Material. Explanatory material, such as references to other standards, references to related sections of this standard, or information related to a rule in this standard, is

included in this standard in the form of informational notes. Such notes are informational only and are not enforceable as requirements of this standard.

Brackets containing section references to another NFPA document are for informational purposes only and are provided as a guide to indicate the source of the extracted text. These bracketed references immediately follow the extracted text.

> Informational Note: The format and language used in this standard follow guidelines established by NFPA and published in the *National Electrical Code Style Manual.* Copies of this manual can be obtained from NFPA.

(D) Informative Annexes. Nonmandatory information relative to the use of this standard is provided in informative annexes. Informative annexes are not part of the requirements of this standard, but are included for information purposes only.

90.5 Formal Interpretations. To promote uniformity of interpretation and application of the provisions of this standard, formal interpretation procedures have been established and are found in the Regulations Governing the Development of NFPA Standards.

Introduction	Introductory and explanatory material
Chapter 1 Safety-Related Work Practices	Applies generally to electrical safety in the workplace
Chapter 2 Safety-Related Maintenance Requirements	Addresses safety-related maintenance requirements
Chapter 3 Safety Requirements for Special Equipment	Modifies the general requirements of Chapter 1
Informative Annexes	Informational material only; not mandatory

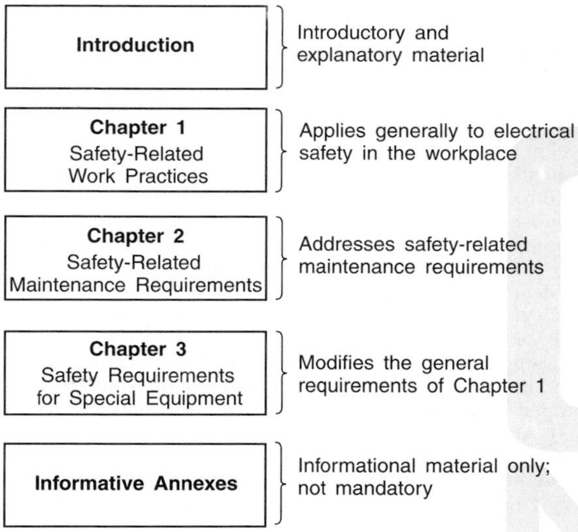

FIGURE 90.3   Standard Arrangement.

Chapter 1   Safety-Related Work Practices

ARTICLE 100
Definitions

Scope. This article contains only those definitions essential to the proper application of this standard. It is not intended to include commonly defined general terms or commonly defined technical terms from related codes and standards. In general, only those terms that are used in two or more articles are defined in Article 100. Other definitions are included in the article in which they are used but may be referenced in Article 100. The definitions in this article shall apply wherever the terms are used throughout this standard.

Accessible (as applied to equipment). Admitting close approach; not guarded by locked doors, elevation, or other effective means. [**70**:100]

Approved. Acceptable to the authority having jurisdiction.

Arc Flash Hazard. A source of possible injury or damage to health associated with the release of energy caused by an electric arc.

> Informational Note No. 1: The likelihood of occurrence of an arc flash incident increases when energized electrical conductors or circuit parts are exposed or when they are within equipment in a guarded or enclosed condition, provided a person is interacting with the equipment in such a manner that could cause an electric arc. An arc flash incident is not likely to occur under normal operating conditions when enclosed energized equipment has been properly installed and maintained. See 110.4(D) for further information.

> Informational Note No. 2: See Table 130.5(C) for examples of tasks that increase the likelihood of an arc flash incident occurring.

Arc Flash Suit. A complete arc-rated clothing and equipment system that covers the entire body, except for the hands and feet.

> Informational Note: An arc flash suit may include pants or overalls, a jacket or a coverall, and a beekeeper-type hood fitted with a face shield.

Δ **Arc Rating.** The value attributed to materials that describes their performance to exposure to an electrical arc discharge. The arc rating is expressed in cal/cm^2 and is derived from the determined value of the arc thermal performance value (ATPV) or energy of breakopen threshold (E_{BT}) (should a material system exhibit a breakopen response below the ATPV value). Arc rating is reported as either ATPV or E_{BT}, whichever is the lower value.

> Informational Note No. 1: Arc-rated clothing or equipment indicates that it has been tested for exposure to an electric arc. Flame-resistant clothing without an arc rating has not been tested for exposure to an electric arc. All arc-rated clothing is also flame resistant.

> Informational Note No. 2: ATPV is defined in ASTM F1959/F1959M, *Standard Test Method for Determining the Arc Rating of Materials for Clothing*, as the incident energy (cal/cm^2) on a material or a multilayer system of materials that results in a 50 percent probability that sufficient heat transfer through the tested specimen is predicted to cause the onset of a second degree skin burn injury based on the Stoll curve.

> Informational Note No. 3: E_{BT} is defined in ASTM F1959/F1959M, *Standard Test Method for Determining the Arc Rating of Materials for Clothing*, as the incident energy (cal/cm^2) on a material or a material system that results in a 50 percent probability of breakopen. Breakopen is a material response evidenced by the formation of one or more holes of a defined size [an area of 1.6 cm^2 (0.5 in.^{2}) or an opening of 2.5 cm (1.0 in.) in any dimension] in the innermost layer of arc-rated material that would allow thermal energy to pass through the material.

Attachment Plug (Plug Cap) (Plug). A device that, by insertion in a receptacle, establishes a connection between the conductors of the attached flexible cord and the conductors connected permanently to the receptacle. [**70**:100]

Authority Having Jurisdiction (AHJ). An organization, office, or individual responsible for enforcing the requirements of a code or standard, or for approving equipment, materials, an installation, or a procedure.

> Informational Note: The phrase "authority having jurisdiction," or its acronym AHJ, is used in NFPA documents in a broad manner, since jurisdictions and approval agencies vary, as do their responsibilities. Where public safety is primary, the authority having jurisdiction may be a federal, state, local, or other regional department or individual such as a fire chief; fire marshal; chief of a fire prevention bureau, labor department, or health department; building official; electrical inspector; or others having statutory authority. For insurance purposes, an insurance inspection department, rating bureau, or other insurance company representative may be the authority having jurisdiction. In many circumstances, the property owner or his or her designated agent assumes the role of the authority having jurisdiction; at government installations, the commanding officer or departmental official may be the authority having jurisdiction.

Automatic. Performing a function without the necessity of human intervention.

Δ **Balaclava.** An arc-rated head-protective fabric that protects the neck and head except for a small portion of the facial area.

> Informational Note: Some balaclava designs protect the neck and head area except for the eyes while others leave the eyes and nose area unprotected.

Barricade. A physical obstruction such as tapes, cones, or A-frame-type wood or metal structures intended to provide a warning and to limit access.

Δ **Barrier.** A physical obstruction that is intended to prevent contact with equipment or energized electrical conductors and circuit parts.

Bonded (Bonding). Connected to establish electrical continuity and conductivity. [**70**:100]

Bonding Conductor or Jumper. A reliable conductor to ensure the required electrical conductivity between metal parts required to be electrically connected. [**70**:100]

Boundary, Arc Flash. When an arc flash hazard exists, an approach limit from an arc source at which incident energy equals 1.2 cal/cm^2 (5 J/cm^2).

> Informational Note: According to the Stoll skin burn injury model, the onset of a second degree burn on unprotected skin is likely to occur at an exposure of 1.2 cal/cm^2 (5 J/cm^2) for one second.

Boundary, Limited Approach. An approach limit at a distance from an exposed energized electrical conductor or circuit part within which a shock hazard exists.

Boundary, Restricted Approach. An approach limit at a distance from an exposed energized electrical conductor or circuit part within which there is an increased likelihood of electric shock, due to electrical arc-over combined with inadvertent movement.

Building. A structure that stands alone or that is cut off from adjoining structures by fire walls with all openings therein protected by approved fire doors. [**70:**100]

Cabinet. An enclosure that is designed for either surface mounting or flush mounting and is provided with a frame, mat, or trim in which a swinging door or doors are or can be hung. [**70:**100]

Circuit Breaker. A device designed to open and close a circuit by nonautomatic means and to open the circuit automatically on a predetermined overcurrent without damage to itself when properly applied within its rating. [**70:**100]

> Informational Note: The automatic opening means can be integral, direct acting with the circuit breaker, or remote from the circuit breaker.

Conductive. Suitable for carrying electric current.

Conductor, Bare. A conductor having no covering or electrical insulation whatsoever. [**70:**100]

Δ **Conductor, Covered.** A conductor encased within material of composition or thickness that is not recognized by *NFPA 70, National Electrical Code,* as electrical insulation. [**70:**100]

Δ **Conductor, Insulated.** A conductor encased within material of composition and thickness that is recognized by *NFPA 70, National Electrical Code,* as electrical insulation. [**70:**100]

Controller. A device or group of devices that serves to govern, in some predetermined manner, the electric power delivered to the apparatus to which it is connected. [**70:**100]

Current-Limiting Overcurrent Protective Device. A device that, when interrupting currents in its current-limiting range, reduces the current flowing in the faulted circuit to a magnitude substantially less than that obtainable in the same circuit if the device were replaced with a solid conductor having comparable impedance.

Cutout. An assembly of a fuse support with either a fuseholder, fuse carrier, or disconnecting blade. The fuseholder or fuse carrier may include a conducting element (fuse link), or may act as the disconnecting blade by the inclusion of a nonfusible member.

De-energized. Free from any electrical connection to a source of potential difference and from electrical charge; not having a potential different from that of the earth.

Device. A unit of an electrical system, other than a conductor, that carries or controls electric energy as its principal function. [**70:**100]

Disconnecting Means. A device, or group of devices, or other means by which the conductors of a circuit can be disconnected from their source of supply. [**70:**100]

Disconnecting (or Isolating) Switch (Disconnector, Isolator). A mechanical switching device used for isolating a circuit or equipment from a source of power.

Dwelling Unit. A single unit providing complete and independent living facilities for one or more persons, including permanent provisions for living, sleeping, cooking, and sanitation. [**70:**100]

Electrical Hazard. A dangerous condition such that contact or equipment failure can result in electric shock, arc flash burn, thermal burn, or arc blast injury.

> Informational Note: Class 2 power supplies, listed low voltage lighting systems, and similar sources are examples of circuits or systems that are not considered an electrical hazard.

Electrical Safety. Identifying hazards associated with the use of electrical energy and taking precautions to reduce the risk associated with those hazards.

Electrical Safety Program. A documented system consisting of electrical safety principles, policies, procedures, and processes that directs activities appropriate for the risk associated with electrical hazards.

Electrically Safe Work Condition. A state in which an electrical conductor or circuit part has been disconnected from energized parts, locked/tagged in accordance with established standards, tested to verify the absence of voltage, and, if necessary, temporarily grounded for personnel protection.

> Informational Note: An electrically safe work condition is not a procedure, it is a state wherein all hazardous electrical conductors or circuit parts to which a worker might be exposed are maintained in a de-energized state for the purpose of temporarily eliminating electrical hazards for the period of time for which the state is maintained.

Enclosed. Surrounded by a case, housing, fence, or wall(s) that prevents persons from unintentionally contacting energized parts.

Enclosure. The case or housing of apparatus — or the fence or walls surrounding an installation to prevent personnel from unintentionally contacting energized electrical conductors or circuit parts or to protect the equipment from physical damage.

Energized. Electrically connected to, or is, a source of voltage. [**70:**100]

Equipment. A general term, including fittings, devices, appliances, luminaires, apparatus, machinery, and the like, used as a part of, or in connection with, an electrical installation. [**70:**100]

Equipment, Arc-Resistant. Equipment designed to withstand the effects of an internal arcing fault and that directs the internally released energy away from the employee.

> Informational Note No. 1: An example of a standard that provides information for arc-resistant equipment is IEEE C37.20.7, *Guide for Testing Switchgear Rated Up to 52 kV for Internal Arcing Faults.*

> Informational Note No. 2: See O.2.4(9) for information on arc-resistant equipment.

Exposed (as applied to energized electrical conductors or circuit parts). Capable of being inadvertently touched or approached nearer than a safe distance by a person. It is applied to electrical conductors or circuit parts that are not suitably guarded, isolated, or insulated.

Exposed (as applied to wiring methods). On or attached to the surface or behind panels designed to allow access. [**70**:100]

Fault Current. The amount of current delivered at a point on the system during a short-circuit condition.

Fault Current, Available. The largest amount of current capable of being delivered at a point on the system during a short-circuit condition.

> Informational Note No. 1: A short circuit can occur during abnormal conditions such as a fault between circuit conductors or a ground fault. See Figure 100.0.

> Informational Note No. 2: If the dc supply is a battery system, the term *available fault current* refers to the prospective short-circuit current.

> Informational Note No. 3: The available fault current varies at different locations within the system due to the location of sources and system impedances.

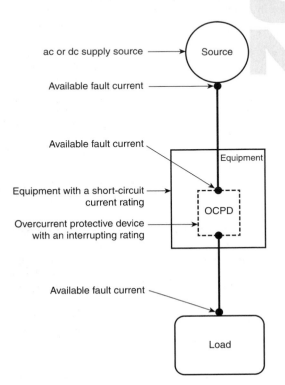

△ FIGURE 100.0   Available Fault Current.

Fitting. An accessory such as a locknut, bushing, or other part of a wiring system that is intended primarily to perform a mechanical rather than an electrical function. [**70**:100]

Fuse. An overcurrent protective device with a circuit-opening fusible part that is heated and severed by the passage of overcurrent through it.

> Informational Note: A fuse comprises all the parts that form a unit capable of performing the prescribed functions. It may or may not be the complete device necessary to connect it into an electrical circuit.

Ground. The earth. [**70**:100]

Ground Fault. An unintentional, electrically conductive connection between an ungrounded conductor of an electrical circuit and the normally non–current-carrying conductors, metallic enclosures, metallic raceways, metallic equipment, or earth. [**70**:100]

Grounded (Grounding). Connected (connecting) to ground or to a conductive body that extends the ground connection. [**70**:100]

Grounded, Solidly. Connected to ground without inserting any resistor or impedance device. [**70**:100]

Grounded Conductor. A system or circuit conductor that is intentionally grounded. [**70**:100]

Ground-Fault Circuit Interrupter (GFCI). A device intended for the protection of personnel that functions to de-energize a circuit or portion thereof within an established period of time when a current to ground exceeds the values established for a Class A device. [**70**:100]

> Informational Note: Class A ground-fault circuit interrupters trip when the current to ground is 6 mA or higher and do not trip when the current to ground is less than 4 mA. For further information, see ANSI/UL 943, *Standard for Ground-Fault Circuit Interrupters.*

Grounding Conductor, Equipment (EGC). The conductive path(s) that provides a ground-fault current path and connects normally non–current-carrying metal parts of equipment together and to the system grounded conductor or to the grounding electrode conductor, or both. [**70**:100]

> Informational Note No. 1: It is recognized that the equipment grounding conductor also performs bonding.

> Informational Note No. 2: See 250.118 of *NFPA 70, National Electrical Code,* for a list of acceptable equipment grounding conductors.

Grounding Electrode. A conducting object through which a direct connection to earth is established. [**70**:100]

Grounding Electrode Conductor. A conductor used to connect the system grounded conductor or the equipment to a grounding electrode or to a point on the grounding electrode system. [**70**:100]

Guarded. Covered, shielded, fenced, enclosed, or otherwise protected by means of suitable covers, casings, barriers, rails, screens, mats, or platforms to remove the likelihood of approach or contact by persons or objects to a point of danger. [**70**:100]

Hazard. A source of possible injury or damage to health.

Hazardous. Involving exposure to at least one hazard.

Shaded text = Revisions.   **△** = Text deletions and figure/table revisions.   • = Section deletions.   **N** = New material.

Incident Energy. The amount of thermal energy impressed on a surface, a certain distance from the source, generated during an electrical arc event. Incident energy is typically expressed in calories per square centimeter (cal/cm²).

Incident Energy Analysis. A component of an arc flash risk assessment used to predict the incident energy of an arc flash for a specified set of conditions.

Insulated. Separated from other conducting surfaces by a dielectric (including air space) offering a high resistance to the passage of current.

Informational Note: When an object is said to be insulated, it is understood to be insulated for the conditions to which it is normally subject. Otherwise, it is, within the purpose of these rules, uninsulated.

Interrupter Switch. A switch capable of making, carrying, and interrupting specified currents.

Interrupting Rating. The highest current at rated voltage that a device is identified to interrupt under standard test conditions. [**70**:100]

Informational Note: Equipment intended to interrupt current at other than fault levels may have its interrupting rating implied in other ratings, such as horsepower or locked rotor current.

Isolated (as applied to location). Not readily accessible to persons unless special means for access are used. [**70**:100]

Labeled. Equipment or materials to which has been attached a label, symbol, or other identifying mark of an organization that is acceptable to the authority having jurisdiction and concerned with product evaluation, that maintains periodic inspection of production of labeled equipment or materials, and by whose labeling the manufacturer indicates compliance with appropriate standards or performance in a specified manner.

Listed. Equipment, materials, or services included in a list published by an organization that is acceptable to the authority having jurisdiction and concerned with evaluation of products or services, that maintains periodic inspection of production of listed equipment or materials or periodic evaluation of services, and whose listing states that either the equipment, material, or service meets appropriate designated standards or has been tested and found suitable for a specified purpose.

Informational Note: The means for identifying listed equipment may vary for each organization concerned with product evaluation; some organizations do not recognize equipment as listed unless it is also labeled. The authority having jurisdiction should utilize the system employed by the listing organization to identify a listed product.

Luminaire. A complete lighting unit consisting of a light source, such as a lamp or lamps, together with the parts designed to position the light source and connect it to the power supply. It may also include parts to protect the light source or the ballast or to distribute the light. A lampholder itself is not a luminaire. [**70**:100]

Maintenance, Condition of. The state of the electrical equipment considering the manufacturers' instructions, manufacturers' recommendations, and applicable industry codes, standards, and recommended practices.

Motor Control Center. An assembly of one or more enclosed sections having a common power bus and principally containing motor control units. [**70**:100]

Outlet. A point on the wiring system at which current is taken to supply utilization equipment. [**70**:100]

Overcurrent. Any current in excess of the rated current of equipment or the ampacity of a conductor. It may result from overload, short circuit, or ground fault. [**70**:100]

Informational Note: A current in excess of rating may be accommodated by certain equipment and conductors for a given set of conditions. Therefore, the rules for overcurrent protection are specific for particular situations.

Overload. Operation of equipment in excess of normal, full-load rating, or of a conductor in excess of rated ampacity that, when it persists for a sufficient length of time, would cause damage or dangerous overheating. A fault, such as a short circuit or ground fault, is not an overload. [**70**:100]

Panelboard. A single panel or group of panel units designed for assembly in the form of a single panel, including buses and automatic overcurrent devices, and equipped with or without switches for the control of light, heat, or power circuits; designed to be placed in a cabinet or cutout box placed in or against a wall, partition, or other support; and accessible only from the front. [**70**:100]

Premises Wiring (System). Interior and exterior wiring, including power, lighting, control, and signal circuit wiring together with all their associated hardware, fittings, and wiring devices, both permanently and temporarily installed. This includes: (a) wiring from the service point or power source to the outlets; or (b) wiring from and including the power source to the outlets where there is no service point.

Such wiring does not include wiring internal to appliances, luminaires, motors, controllers, motor control centers, and similar equipment. [**70**:100]

Informational Note: Power sources include, but are not limited to, interconnected or stand-alone batteries, solar photovoltaic systems, other distributed generation systems, or generators.

Qualified Person. One who has demonstrated skills and knowledge related to the construction and operation of electrical equipment and installations and has received safety training to identify the hazards and reduce the associated risk.

Raceway. An enclosed channel of metal or nonmetallic materials designed expressly for holding wires, cables, or busbars, with additional functions as permitted in this standard. [**70**:100]

Δ **Receptacle.** A contact device installed at the outlet for the connection of an attachment plug, or for the direct connection of electrical utilization equipment designed to mate with the corresponding contact device. A single receptacle is a single contact device with no other contact device on the same yoke. A multiple receptacle is two or more contact devices on the same yoke. [**70**:100]

Risk. A combination of the likelihood of occurrence of injury or damage to health and the severity of injury or damage to health that results from a hazard.

Risk Assessment. An overall process that identifies hazards, estimates the likelihood of occurrence of injury or damage to health, estimates the potential severity of injury or damage to health, and determines if protective measures are required.

Informational Note: As used in this standard, *arc flash risk assessment* and *shock risk assessment* are types of risk assessments.

Service Drop. The overhead conductors between the utility electric supply system and the service point. [**70**:100]

Service Lateral. The underground conductors between the utility electric supply system and the service point. [**70**:100]

Service Point. The point of connection between the facilities of the serving utility and the premises wiring. [**70**:100]

Informational Note: The service point can be described as the point of demarcation between where the serving utility ends and the premises wiring begins. The serving utility generally specifies the location of the service point based on the conditions of service.

Shock Hazard. A source of possible injury or damage to health associated with current through the body caused by contact or approach to exposed energized electrical conductors or circuit parts.

Informational Note: Injury and damage to health resulting from shock is dependent on the magnitude of the electrical current, the power source frequency (e.g., 60 Hz, 50 Hz, dc), and the path and time duration of current through the body. The physiological reaction ranges from perception, muscular contractions, inability to let go, ventricular fibrillation, tissue burns, and death.

Short-Circuit Current Rating. The prospective symmetrical fault current at a nominal voltage to which an apparatus or system is able to be connected without sustaining damage exceeding defined acceptance criteria. [**70**:100]

Single-Line Diagram. A diagram that shows, by means of single lines and graphic symbols, the course of an electric circuit or system of circuits and the component devices or parts used in the circuit or system.

Special Permission. The written consent of the authority having jurisdiction. [**70**:100]

Step Potential. A ground potential gradient difference that can cause current flow from foot to foot through the body.

Structure. That which is built or constructed. [**70**:100]

Switch, Isolating. A switch intended for isolating an electric circuit from the source of power. It has no interrupting rating, and it is intended to be operated only after the circuit has been opened by some other means. [**70**:100]

Switchboard. A large single panel, frame, or assembly of panels on which are mounted on the face, back, or both, switches, overcurrent and other protective devices, buses, and usually instruments. These assemblies are generally accessible from the rear as well as from the front and are not intended to be installed in cabinets. [**70**:100]

Switchgear, Metal-Clad. A switchgear assembly completely enclosed on all sides and top with sheet metal, having drawout switching and interrupting devices, and all live parts enclosed within grounded metal compartments.

Switchgear, Metal-Enclosed. A switchgear assembly completely enclosed on all sides and top with sheet metal (except for ventilating openings and inspection windows), containing primary power circuit switching, interrupting devices, or both, with buses and connections. This assembly may include control and auxiliary devices. Access to the interior of the enclosure is provided by doors, removable covers, or both. Metal-enclosed switchgear is available in non-arc-resistant or arc-resistant constructions.

Switching Device. A device designed to close, open, or both, one or more electric circuits.

Touch Potential. A ground potential gradient difference that can cause current flow from hand to hand, hand to foot, or another path, other than foot to foot, through the body.

Ungrounded. Not connected to ground or to a conductive body that extends the ground connection. [**70**:100]

Unqualified Person. A person who is not a qualified person.

Utilization Equipment. Equipment that utilizes electric energy for electronic, electromechanical, chemical, heating, lighting, or similar purposes. [**70**:100]

Voltage (of a Circuit). The greatest root-mean-square (rms) (effective) difference of potential between any two conductors of the circuit concerned. [**70**:100]

Informational Note: Some systems, such as three-phase 4-wire, single-phase 3-wire, and 3-wire direct-current, may have various circuits of various voltages.

Voltage, Nominal. A nominal value assigned to a circuit or system for the purpose of conveniently designating its voltage class (e.g., 120/240 volts, 480Y/277 volts, 600 volts). [**70**:100]

Informational Note No. 1: The actual voltage at which a circuit operates can vary from the nominal within a range that permits satisfactory operation of equipment.

Informational Note No. 2: See ANSI C84.1, *Electric Power Systems and Equipment — Voltage Ratings (60 Hz)*.

Informational Note No. 3: Certain battery units are rated at nominal 48 volts dc but have a charging float voltage up to 58 volts. In dc applications, 60 volts is used to cover the entire range of float voltages.

Δ **Working Distance.** The distance between a person's face and chest area and a prospective arc source.

Informational Note: Incident energy increases as the distance from the arc source decreases. See 130.5(C)(1) for further information.

Working On (energized electrical conductors or circuit parts). Intentionally coming in contact with energized electrical conductors or circuit parts with the hands, feet, or other body parts, with tools, probes, or with test equipment, regardless of the personal protective equipment (PPE) a person is wearing. There are two categories of "working on": *Diagnostic (testing)* is taking readings or measurements of electrical equipment, conductors, or circuit parts with approved test equipment that does not require making any physical change to the electrical equipment, conductors, or circuit parts. *Repair* is any physical alteration of electrical equipment, conductors, or circuit parts (such as making or tightening connections, removing or replacing components, etc.).

ARTICLE 105
Application of Safety-Related Work Practices and Procedures

105.1 Scope. Chapter 1 covers electrical safety-related work practices and procedures for employees who are exposed to an electrical hazard in workplaces covered in the scope of this standard.

105.2 Purpose. These practices and procedures are intended to provide for employee safety relative to electrical hazards in the workplace.

Informational Note: For general categories of electrical hazards, see Informative Annex K.

105.3 Responsibility.

(A) Employer Responsibility. The employer shall have the following responsibilities:

(1) Establish, document, and implement the safety-related work practices and procedures required by this standard.
(2) Provide employees with training in the employer's safety-related work practices and procedures.

(B) Employee Responsibility. The employee shall comply with the safety-related work practices and procedures provided by the employer.

105.5 Organization. Chapter 1 of this standard is divided into five articles. Article 100 provides definitions for terms used in one or more of the chapters of this document. Article 105 provides for application of safety-related work practices and procedures. Article 110 provides general requirements for electrical safety-related work practices and procedures. Article 120 provides requirements for establishing an electrically safe work condition. Article 130 provides requirements for work involving electrical hazards.

ARTICLE 110
General Requirements for Electrical Safety-Related Work Practices

110.1 Priority. Hazard elimination shall be the first priority in the implementation of safety-related work practices.

Informational Note No. 1: Elimination is the risk control method listed first in the hierarchy of risk control identified in 110.5(H)(3). See Annex F for examples of hazard elimination.

Informational Note No. 2: An electrically safe work condition is a state wherein all hazardous electrical conductors or circuit parts to which a worker might be exposed are placed and maintained in a de-energized state, for the purpose of temporarily eliminating electrical hazards. See Article 120 for requirements to establish an electrically safe work condition for the period of time for which the state is maintained. See Informative Annex F for information regarding the hierarchy of risk control and hazard elimination.

110.2 General. Electrical conductors and circuit parts shall not be considered to be in an electrically safe work condition until all of the requirements of Article 120 have been met.

Safe work practices applicable to the circuit voltage and energy level shall be used in accordance with Article 110 and Article 130 until such time that electrical conductors and circuit parts are in an electrically safe work condition.

Informational Note: See 120.5 for the steps to establish and verify an electrically safe work condition.

110.3 Electrically Safe Work Condition. Energized electrical conductors and circuit parts operating at voltages equal to or greater than 50 volts shall be put into an electrically safe work condition before an employee performs work if any of the following conditions exist:

(1) The employee is within the limited approach boundary.
(2) The employee interacts with equipment where conductors or circuit parts are not exposed but an increased likelihood of injury from an exposure to an arc flash hazard exists.

110.4 Energized Work.

(A) Additional Hazards or Increased Risk. Energized work shall be permitted where the employer can demonstrate that de-energizing introduces additional hazards or increased risk.

Informational Note: Examples of additional hazards or increased risk include, but are not limited to, interruption of life-support equipment, deactivation of emergency alarm systems, and shutdown of hazardous location ventilation equipment.

(B) Infeasibility. Energized work shall be permitted where the employer can demonstrate that the task to be performed is infeasible in a de-energized state due to equipment design or operational limitations.

Informational Note: Examples of work that might be performed within the limited approach boundary of exposed energized electrical conductors or circuit parts because of infeasibility due to equipment design or operational limitations include performing diagnostics and testing (for example, start-up or trouble-shooting) of electric circuits that can only be performed with the circuit energized and work on circuits that form an integral part of a continuous process that would otherwise need to be completely shut down in order to permit work on one circuit or piece of equipment.

(C) Equipment Operating at Less Than 50 Volts. Energized electrical conductors and circuit parts that operate at less than 50 volts shall not be required to be de-energized where the capacity of the source and any overcurrent protection between the energy source and the worker are considered and it is determined that there will be no increased exposure to electrical burns or to explosion due to electric arcs.

(D) Normal Operating Condition. Normal operation of electric equipment shall be permitted where a normal operating condition exists. A normal operating condition exists when all of the following conditions are satisfied:

(1) The equipment is properly installed.
(2) The equipment is properly maintained.
(3) The equipment is used in accordance with instructions included in the listing and labeling and in accordance with manufacturer's instructions.

(4) The equipment doors are closed and secured.
(5) All equipment covers are in place and secured.
(6) There is no evidence of impending failure.

Informational Note: The phrase *properly installed* means that the equipment is installed in accordance with applicable industry codes and standards and the manufacturer's recommendations. The phrase *properly maintained* means that the equipment has been maintained in accordance with the manufacturer's recommendations and applicable industry codes and standards. The phrase *evidence of impending failure* means that there is evidence such as arcing, overheating, loose or bound equipment parts, visible damage, or deterioration.

110.5 Electrical Safety Program.

△ **(A) General.** The employer shall implement and document an overall electrical safety program that directs activity appropriate to the risk associated with electrical hazards.

Informational Note No. 1: Safety-related work practices such as verification of proper maintenance and installation, alerting techniques, auditing requirements, and training requirements provided in this standard are administrative controls and part of an overall electrical safety program.

Informational Note No. 2: See Informative Annex P for information on implementing an electrical safety program within an employer's occupational health and safety management system.

Informational Note No. 3: IEEE 3007.1, *Recommended Practice for the Operation and Management of Industrial and Commercial Power Systems*, provides additional guidance for the implementation of the electrical safety program.

Informational Note No. 4: IEEE 3007.3, *Recommended Practice for Electrical Safety in Industrial and Commercial Power Systems*, provides additional guidance for electrical safety in the workplace.

(B) Inspection. The electrical safety program shall include elements to verify that newly installed or modified electrical equipment or systems have been inspected to comply with applicable installation codes and standards prior to being placed into service.

(C) Condition of Maintenance. The electrical safety program shall include elements that consider condition of maintenance of electrical equipment and systems.

(D) Awareness and Self-Discipline. The electrical safety program shall be designed to provide an awareness of the potential electrical hazards to employees who work in an environment with the presence of electrical hazards. The program shall be developed to provide the required self-discipline for all employees who must perform work that may involve electrical hazards. The program shall instill safety principles and controls.

(E) Electrical Safety Program Principles. The electrical safety program shall identify the principles upon which it is based.

Informational Note: For examples of typical electrical safety program principles, see Informative Annex E.

(F) Electrical Safety Program Controls. An electrical safety program shall identify the controls by which it is measured and monitored.

Informational Note: For examples of typical electrical safety program controls, see Informative Annex E.

(G) Electrical Safety Program Procedures. An electrical safety program shall identify the procedures to be utilized before work is started by employees exposed to an electrical hazard.

Informational Note: For an example of a typical electrical safety program procedure, see Informative Annex E.

(H) Risk Assessment Procedure. The electrical safety program shall include a risk assessment procedure and shall comply with 110.5(H)(1) through 110.5(H)(3).

△ **(1) Elements of a Risk Assessment Procedure.** The risk assessment procedure shall address employee exposure to electrical hazards and shall identify the process to be used before work is started to carry out the following:

(1) Identify hazards
(2) Assess risks
(3) Implement risk control according to the hierarchy of risk control methods

Informational Note No. 1: The risk assessment procedure could include identifying when a second person could be required and the training and equipment that person should have.

Informational Note No. 2: For more information regarding risk assessment and the hierarchy of risk control, see Informative Annex F.

(2) Human Error. The risk assessment procedure shall address the potential for human error and its negative consequences on people, processes, the work environment, and equipment relative to the electrical hazards in the workplace.

Informational Note: The potential for human error varies with factors such as tasks and the work environment. See Informative Annex Q.

△ **(3) Hierarchy of Risk Control Methods.** The risk assessment procedure shall require that preventive and protective risk control methods be implemented in accordance with the following hierarchy:

(1) Elimination
(2) Substitution
(3) Engineering controls
(4) Awareness
(5) Administrative controls
(6) PPE

Informational Note No. 1: Elimination, substitution, and engineering controls are the most effective methods to reduce risk as they are usually applied at the source of possible injury or damage to health and they are less likely to be affected by human error. Awareness, administrative controls, and PPE are the least effective methods to reduce risk as they are not applied at the source and they are more likely to be affected by human error.

Informational Note No. 2: See Informative Annex F for more information regarding the hierarchy of risk control methods and examples of those methods.

(I) Job Safety Planning and Job Briefing. Before starting each job that involves exposure to electrical hazards, the employee in charge shall complete a job safety plan and conduct a job briefing with the employees involved.

(1) Job Safety Planning. The job safety plan shall be in accordance with the following:

(1) Be completed by a qualified person
(2) Be documented

(3) Include the following information:

   a. A description of the job and the individual tasks

   b. Identification of the electrical hazards associated with each task

   c. A shock risk assessment in accordance with 130.4 for tasks involving a shock hazard

   d. An arc flash risk assessment in accordance with 130.5 for tasks involving an arc flash hazard

   e. Work procedures involved, special precautions, and energy source controls

Informational Note: For an example of a job safety planning checklist see Figure I.2.

(2) Job Briefing. The job briefing shall cover the job safety plan and the information on the energized electrical work permit, if a permit is required.

Δ **(3) Change in Scope.** Additional job safety planning and job briefings shall be held if changes occur during the course of the work that might affect the safety of employees.

Informational Note: For an example of a job briefing checklist, see Figure I.1.

(J) Incident Investigations. The electrical safety program shall include elements to investigate electrical incidents.

Informational Note: Electrical incidents include events or occurrences that result in, or could have resulted in, a fatality, an injury, or damage to health. Incidents that do not result in fatality, injury, or damage to health are commonly referred to as a "close call" or "near miss."

N **(K) Electrically Safe Work Condition Policy.** An electrical safety program shall include an electrically safe work condition policy that complies with 110.3.

N **(L) Lockout/Tagout Program.** The electrical safety program shall include the information required by one of the following:

(1) A lockout/tagout program in accordance with 120.1(A)

(2) A reference to the employer's lockout/tagout program established in accordance with 120.1(A)

(M) Auditing.

(1) Electrical Safety Program Audit. The electrical safety program shall be audited to verify that the principles and procedures of the electrical safety program are in compliance with this standard. Audits shall be performed at intervals not to exceed 3 years.

(2) Field Work Audit. Field work shall be audited to verify that the requirements contained in the procedures of the electrical safety program are being followed. When the auditing determines that the principles and procedures of the electrical safety program are not being followed, the appropriate revisions to the training program or revisions to the procedures shall be made. Audits shall be performed at intervals not to exceed 1 year.

(3) Lockout/Tagout Program and Procedure Audit. The lockout/tagout program and procedures required by Article 120 shall be audited by a qualified person at intervals not to exceed 1 year. The audit shall cover at least one lockout/tagout in progress. The audit shall be designed to identify and correct deficiencies in the following:

(1) The lockout/tagout program and procedures

(2) The lockout/tagout training

(3) Worker execution of the lockout/tagout procedure

(4) Documentation. The audits required by 110.5(M) shall be documented.

110.6 Training Requirements.

(A) Electrical Safety Training. The training requirements contained in 110.6(A) shall apply to employees exposed to an electrical hazard when the risk associated with that hazard is not reduced to a safe level by the applicable electrical installation requirements. Such employees shall be trained to understand the specific hazards associated with electrical energy. They shall be trained in safety-related work practices and procedural requirements, as necessary, to provide protection from the electrical hazards associated with their respective job or task assignments. Employees shall be trained to identify and understand the relationship between electrical hazards and possible injury.

Informational Note: For further information concerning installation requirements, see *NFPA 70, National Electrical Code.*

(1) Qualified Person. A qualified person shall be trained and knowledgeable in the construction and operation of equipment or a specific work method and be trained to identify and avoid the electrical hazards that might be present with respect to that equipment or work method.

   (a) Such persons shall also be familiar with the proper use of the special precautionary techniques, applicable electrical policies and procedures, PPE, insulating and shielding materials, and insulated tools and test equipment.

   (b) A person can be considered qualified with respect to certain equipment and tasks but still be unqualified for others.

   (c) Such persons permitted to work within the limited approach boundary shall, at a minimum, be additionally trained in all of the following:

(1) Skills and techniques necessary to distinguish exposed energized electrical conductors and circuit parts from other parts of electrical equipment

(2) Skills and techniques necessary to determine the nominal voltage of exposed energized electrical conductors and circuit parts

(3) Approach distances specified in Table 130.4(E)(a) and Table 130.4(E)(b) and the corresponding voltages to which the qualified person will be exposed

(4) Decision-making process necessary to be able to do the following:

   a. Perform the job safety planning

   b. Identify electrical hazards

   c. Assess the associated risk

   d. Select the appropriate risk control methods from the hierarchy of controls identified in 110.5(H)(3), including PPE

   (d) An employee who is undergoing on-the-job training for the purpose of obtaining the skills and knowledge necessary to be considered a qualified person, and who in the course of such training demonstrates an ability to perform specific duties safely at his or her level of training, and who is under the direct supervision of a qualified person shall be considered to be a qualified person for the performance of those specific duties.

   (e) Employees shall be trained to select an appropriate test instrument and shall demonstrate how to use a device to verify the absence of voltage, including interpreting indications provided by the device. The training shall include information that enables the employee to understand all limitations of each test instrument that might be used.

(f) The employer shall determine through regular supervision or through inspections conducted on at least an annual basis that each employee is complying with the safety-related work practices required by this standard.

(2) Unqualified Persons. Unqualified persons shall be trained in, and be familiar with, any electrical safety-related practices necessary for their safety.

Δ **(3) Additional Training and Retraining.** Additional training and retraining in safety-related work practices and applicable changes in this standard shall be performed at intervals not to exceed 3 years. An employee shall receive additional training or retraining if any of the following conditions exists:

(1) The supervision or annual inspections indicate the employee is not complying with the safety-related work practices.

(2) New technology, new types of equipment, or changes in procedures necessitate the use of safety-related work practices different from those that the employee would normally use.

(3) The employee needs to review tasks that are performed less often than once per year.

(4) The employee needs to review safety-related work practices not normally used by the employee during regular job duties.

(5) The employee's job duties change.

(4) Type of Training. The training required by 110.6(A) shall be classroom, on-the-job, or a combination of the two. The type and extent of the training provided shall be determined by the risk to the employee.

> Informational Note: Classroom training can include interactive electronic or interactive web-based training components.

(5) Electrical Safety Training Documentation. The employer shall document that each employee has received the training required by 110.6(A). This documentation shall be in accordance with the following:

(1) Be made when the employee demonstrates proficiency in the work practices involved

(2) Be retained for the duration of the employee's employment

(3) Contain the content of the training, each employee's name, and dates of training

> Informational Note No. 1: Content of the training could include one or more of the following: course syllabus, course curriculum, outline, table of contents, or training objectives.

> Informational Note No. 2: Employment records that indicate that an employee has received the required training are an acceptable means of meeting this requirement.

(B) Lockout/Tagout Procedure Training.

Δ **(1) Initial Training.** Employees involved in the lockout/tagout procedures required by 120.2(B) shall be trained in the following:

(1) The lockout/tagout procedures

(2) Their responsibility in the execution of the procedures

(2) Retraining. Retraining in the lockout/tagout procedures shall be performed as follows:

(1) When the procedures are revised

(2) At intervals not to exceed 3 years

(3) When supervision or annual inspections indicate that the employee is not complying with the lockout/tagout procedures

(3) Lockout/Tagout Training Documentation.

(a) The employer shall document that each employee has received the training required by 110.6(B).

(b) The documentation shall be made when the employee demonstrates proficiency in the work practices involved.

(c) The documentation shall contain the content of the training, each employee's name, and the dates of the training.

> Informational Note: Content of the training could include one or more of the following: course syllabus, course curriculum, outline, table of contents, or training objectives.

(C) Emergency Response Training.

(1) Contact Release. Employees exposed to shock hazards and those responsible for the safe release of victims from contact with energized electrical conductors or circuit parts shall be trained in methods of safe release. Refresher training shall occur annually.

(2) First Aid, Emergency Response, and Resuscitation.

(a) Employees responsible for responding to medical emergencies shall be trained in first aid and emergency procedures.

(b) Employees responsible for responding to medical emergencies shall be trained in cardiopulmonary resuscitation (CPR).

(c) Employees responsible for responding to medical emergencies shall be trained in the use of an automated external defibrillator (AED) if an employer's emergency response plan includes the use of this device.

(d) Training shall occur at a frequency that satisfies the requirements of the certifying body.

> Informational Note: Employees responsible for responding to medical emergencies might not be first responders or medical professionals. Such employees could be a second person, a safety watch, or a craftsperson.

(3) Training Verification. Employers shall verify at least annually that employee training required by 110.6(C) is current.

(4) Documentation. The employer shall document that the training required by 110.6(C) has occurred.

110.7 Host and Contract Employers' Responsibilities.

(A) Host Employer Responsibilities.

(1) The host employer shall inform contract employers of the following:

(1) Known hazards that are covered by this standard, that are related to the contract employer's work, and that might not be recognized by the contract employer or its employees

(2) Information about the employer's installation that the contract employer needs to make the assessments required by Chapter 1

(2) The host employer shall report observed contract employer–related violations of this standard to the contract employer.

> Informational Note: Examples of a host employer can include owner or their designee, construction manager, general contractor, or employer.

(B) Contract Employer Responsibilities.

(1) The contract employer shall ensure that each of his or her employees is instructed in the hazards communicated to the contract employer by the host employer. This instruction shall be in addition to the basic training required by this standard.

(2) The contract employer shall ensure that each of his or her employees follows the work practices required by this standard and safety-related work rules required by the host employer.

(3) The contract employer shall advise the host employer of the following:

(1) Any unique hazards presented by the contract employer's work

(2) Hazards identified during the course of work by the contract employer that were not communicated by the host employer

(3) The measures the contractor took to correct any violations reported by the host employer under 110.7(A)(2) and to prevent such violation from recurring in the future

(C) Documentation. Where the host employer has knowledge of hazards covered by this standard that are related to the contract employer's work, there shall be a documented meeting between the host employer and the contract employer.

> Informational Note to 110.7: On multi-employer work sites (in all industry sectors), more than one employer can be responsible for identifying hazardous conditions and creating safe work practices.

110.8 Test Instruments and Equipment.

(A) Testing. Only qualified persons shall perform tasks such as testing, troubleshooting, and voltage measuring on electrical equipment where an electrical hazard exists.

(B) Rating. Test instruments, equipment, and their accessories shall be as follows:

(1) Rated for circuits and equipment where they are utilized

(2) Approved for the purpose

(3) Used in accordance with any instructions provided by the manufacturer

> Informational Note: See UL 61010-1, *Safety Requirements for Electrical Equipment for Measurement, Control, and Laboratory Use – Part 1: General Requirements*, for rating and design requirements for voltage measurement and test instruments intended for use on electrical systems 1000 volts and below and UL 61010-2-033, *Safety Requirements for Electrical Equipment for Measurement, Control, and Laboratory Use — Part 2-033: Particular Requirements for Hand-Held Multimeters and Other Meters, for Domestic and Professional use, Capable of Measuring Mains Voltage.*

(C) Design. Test instruments, equipment, and their accessories shall be designed for the environment to which they will be exposed and for the manner in which they will be utilized.

(D) Visual Inspection and Repair. Test instruments and equipment and all associated test leads, cables, power cords, probes, and connectors shall be visually inspected for external defects and damage before each use. If there is a defect or evidence of damage that might expose an employee to injury, the defective or damaged item shall be removed from service. No employee shall use it until a person(s) qualified to perform the repairs and tests that are necessary to render the equipment safe has done so.

(E) Operation Verification. When test instruments are used for testing the absence of voltage on conductors or circuit parts operating at voltages equal to or greater than 50 volts, the operation of the test instrument shall be verified on any known voltage source before and after an absence of voltage test is performed.

110.9 Portable Cord- and-Plug-Connected Electric Equipment. This section applies to the use of cord- and plug-connected equipment, including cord- and plug-connected test instruments and cord sets (extension cords).

(A) Handling and Storage. Portable equipment shall be handled and stored in a manner that will not cause damage. Flexible electric cords connected to equipment shall not be used for raising or lowering the equipment. Flexible cords shall not be fastened with staples or hung in such a fashion as could damage the outer jacket or insulation.

(B) Grounding-Type Equipment.

(a) A flexible cord used with grounding-type utilization equipment shall contain an equipment grounding conductor.

(b) Attachment plugs and receptacles shall not be connected or altered in a manner that would interrupt continuity of the equipment grounding conductor. Additionally, these devices shall not be altered in order to allow use in a manner that was not intended by the manufacturer.

(c) Adapters that interrupt the continuity of the equipment grounding conductor shall not be used.

Δ **(C) Visual Inspection and Repair of Portable Cord- and Plug-Connected Equipment and Flexible Cord Sets.**

(a) *Frequency of Inspection.* Before each use, portable cord- and plug-connected equipment shall be visually inspected for external defects (such as loose parts or deformed and missing pins) and for evidence of possible internal damage (such as a pinched or crushed outer jacket).

Exception: Stationary cord- and plug-connected equipment that remain connected once they are put in place and are installed such that the cord and plug are not subject to physical damage during normal use shall not be required to be visually inspected until they are relocated or repaired.

(b) *Defective Equipment.* If there is a defect or evidence of damage that might expose an employee to injury, the defective or damaged item shall be removed from service. No employee shall use it until a person(s) qualified to perform the repairs and tests necessary to render the equipment safe has done so.

(c) *Proper Mating.* When an attachment plug is to be connected to a receptacle, the relationship of the plug and receptacle contacts shall first be checked to ensure that they are of mating configurations.

△ **(D) Conductive or Wet Work Locations.** Portable cord-and-plug-connected electric equipment used in conductive or wet work locations shall be approved for use in those locations. In work locations where employees are likely to contact or be drenched with water or conductive liquids, ground-fault circuit-interrupter protection for personnel shall be used.

> Informational Note: The risk assessment procedure can also include identifying when the use of portable tools and equipment powered by sources other than 120 volts ac, such as batteries, air, and hydraulics, should be used to minimize the potential for injury from electrical hazards for tasks performed in conductive or wet locations.

(E) Connecting Attachment Plugs.

    (a) Employees' hands shall not be wet when plugging and unplugging flexible cords and cord- and plug-connected equipment if energized equipment is involved.

    (b) Energized plug and receptacle connections shall be handled only with insulating protective equipment if the condition of the connection could provide a conductive path to the employee's hand (e.g, if a cord connector is wet from being immersed in water).

    (c) Locking-type connectors shall be secured after connection.

(F) Manufacturer's Instructions. Portable equipment shall be used in accordance with the manufacturer's instructions and safety warnings.

110.10 Ground-Fault Circuit-Interrupter (GFCI) Protection.

(A) General. Employees shall be provided with ground-fault circuit-interrupter (GFCI) protection where required by applicable state, federal, or local codes and standards. Listed cord sets or devices incorporating listed GFCI protection for personnel identified for portable use shall be permitted.

(B) Maintenance and Construction. GFCI protection shall be provided where an employee is operating or using cord sets (extension cords) or cord- and plug-connected tools related to maintenance and construction activity supplied by 125-volt, 15-, 20-, or 30-ampere circuits. Where employees operate or use equipment supplied by greater than 125-volt, 15-, 20-, or 30-ampere circuits, GFCI protection or an assured equipment grounding conductor program shall be implemented.

> Informational Note: Where an assured equipment grounding conductor program is used, a special purpose ground-fault circuit interrupter may provide additional protection. See Informative Annex O.

(C) Outdoors. GFCI protection shall be provided when an employee is outdoors and operating or using cord sets (extension cords) or cord- and plug-connected equipment supplied by 125-volt, 15-, 20-, or 30-ampere circuits. Where employees working outdoors operate or use equipment supplied by greater than 125-volt, 15-, 20-, or 30-ampere circuits, GFCI protection or an assured equipment grounding conductor program shall be implemented.

> Informational Note: Where an assured equipment grounding conductor program is used, a special purpose ground-fault circuit interrupter may provide additional protection. See Informative Annex O.

(D) Testing Ground-Fault Circuit-Interrupter Protection Devices. GFCI protection devices shall be tested in accordance with the manufacturer's instructions.

110.11 Overcurrent Protection Modification. Overcurrent protection of circuits and conductors shall not be modified, even on a temporary basis, beyond what is permitted by applicable portions of electrical codes and standards dealing with overcurrent protection.

> Informational Note: For further information concerning electrical codes and standards dealing with overcurrent protection, refer to Article 240 of NFPA 70, National Electrical Code.

N **110.12 Equipment Use.** Equipment shall be used in accordance with the manufacturer's instructions.

ARTICLE 120
Establishing an Electrically Safe Work Condition

120.1 Lockout/Tagout Program.

(A) General. Each employer shall establish, document, and implement a lockout/tagout program. The lockout/tagout program shall specify lockout/tagout procedures to safeguard workers from exposure to electrical hazards. The lockout/tagout program and procedures shall also incorporate the following:

(1) Be applicable to the experience and training of the workers and conditions in the workplace
(2) Meet the requirements of Article 120
(3) Apply to fixed, permanently installed equipment, temporarily installed equipment, and portable equipment

(B) Employer Responsibilities. The employer shall be responsible for the following:

(1) Providing the equipment necessary to execute lockout/tagout procedures
(2) Providing lockout/tagout training to workers in accordance with 110.6(B)
(3) Auditing the lockout/tagout program in accordance with 110.5(M)(3)
(4) Auditing execution of the lockout/tagout procedures in accordance with 110.5(M)(3)

> Informational Note: For an example of a lockout/tagout program, see Informative Annex G.

120.2 Lockout/Tagout Principles.

(A) Employee Involvement. Each person who could be exposed directly or indirectly to a source of electrical energy shall be involved in the lockout/tagout procedure.

> Informational Note: An example of direct exposure is the qualified electrician who works on the motor starter control, the power circuits, or the motor. An example of indirect exposure is the person who works on the coupling between the motor and compressor.

(B) Lockout/Tagout Procedure. A lockout/tagout procedure shall be developed on the basis of the existing electrical equipment and system and shall use suitable documentation including up-to-date drawings and diagrams. The procedure shall meet the requirements of applicable codes, standards, and regulations for lockout and tagging of electrical sources.

(C) Control of Energy. All sources of electrical energy shall be controlled in such a way as to minimize employee exposure to electrical hazards.

(D) Electrical Circuit Interlocks. Documentation, including up-to-date drawings and diagrams, shall be reviewed to ensure that no electrical circuit interlock operation can result in re-energizing the circuit being worked on.

(E) Control Devices. Locks/tags shall be installed only on circuit disconnecting means. Control devices, such as push-buttons or selector switches, shall not be used as the primary isolating device.

(F) Identification. The lockout/tagout device shall be unique and readily identifiable as a lockout/tagout device.

(G) Coordination. The following items are necessary for coordinating the lockout/tagout procedure:

(1) The electrical lockout/tagout procedure shall be coordinated with all other employer's procedures for control of exposure to electrical energy sources such that all employer's procedural requirements are adequately addressed on a site basis.

(2) The procedure for control of exposure to electrical hazards shall be coordinated with other procedures for control of other hazardous energy based on similar or identical concepts.

(3) Electrical lockout/tagout devices shall be permitted to be similar to lockout/tagout devices for control of other hazardous energy sources, such as pneumatic, hydraulic, thermal, and mechanical, if such devices are used only for control of hazardous energy and for no other purpose.

(H) Forms of Control of Hazardous Electrical Energy. Two forms of hazardous electrical energy control shall be permitted: simple lockout/tagout and complex lockout/tagout *[see 120.4]*. For the simple lockout/tagout, the qualified person shall be in charge. For the complex lockout/tagout, the person in charge shall have overall responsibility.

120.3 Lockout/Tagout Equipment.

(A) Lock Application. Energy isolation devices for machinery or equipment installed after January 2, 1990, shall be capable of accepting a lockout device.

(B) Lockout/Tagout Device. Each employer shall supply, and employees shall use, lockout/tagout devices and equipment necessary to execute the requirements of 120.3. Locks and tags used for control of exposure to electrical hazards shall be unique, shall be readily identifiable as lockout/tagout devices, and shall be used for no other purpose.

(C) Lockout Device. The lockout device shall meet the following requirements:

(1) A lockout device shall include a lock — either keyed or combination.

(2) The lockout device shall include a method of identifying the individual who installed the lockout device.

(3) A lockout device shall be permitted to be only a lock, if the lock is readily identifiable as a lockout device, in addition to having a means of identifying the person who installed the lock, provided that all of the following conditions exist:

(a) Only one circuit or piece of equipment is de-energized.

(b) The lockout period does not extend beyond the work shift.

(c) Employees exposed to the hazards associated with re-energizing the circuit or equipment are familiar with this procedure.

(4) Lockout devices shall be attached to prevent operation of the disconnecting means without resorting to undue force or the use of tools.

(5) Where a tag is used in conjunction with a lockout device, the tag shall contain a statement prohibiting unauthorized operation of the disconnecting means or unauthorized removal of the device.

(6) Lockout devices shall be suitable for the environment and for the duration of the lockout.

(7) Whether keyed or combination locks are used, the key or combination shall remain in the possession of the individual installing the lock or the person in charge, when provided by the established procedure.

(D) Tagout Device. The tagout device shall meet the following requirements:

(1) A tagout device shall include a tag together with an attachment means.

(2) The tagout device shall be readily identifiable as a tagout device and suitable for the environment and duration of the tagout.

(3) A tagout device attachment means shall be capable of withstanding at least 224.4 N (50 lb) of force exerted at a right angle to the disconnecting means surface. The tag attachment means shall be nonreusable, attachable by hand, self-locking, nonreleasable, and equal to an all-environmental tolerant nylon cable tie.

(4) Tags shall contain a statement prohibiting unauthorized operation of the disconnecting means or removal of the tag.

(5) A hold card tagging tool on an overhead conductor in conjunction with a hotline tool to install the tagout device safely on a disconnect that is isolated from the work(s) shall be permitted. Where a hold card is used, the tagout procedure shall include the method of accounting for personnel who are working under the protection of the hold card.

120.4 Lockout/Tagout Procedures. The employer shall maintain a copy of the procedures required by this section and shall make the procedures available to all employees.

(A) Planning. The procedure shall require planning, including the requirements of 120.4(A)(1) through 120.4(B)(14).

(1) Locating Sources. Up-to-date single-line drawings shall be considered a primary reference source for such information. When up-to-date drawings are not available, the employer shall be responsible for ensuring that an equally effective means of locating all sources of energy is employed.

(2) Exposed Persons. The plan shall identify persons who might be exposed to an electrical hazard and the PPE required during the execution of the job or task.

(3) Person in Charge. The plan shall identify the person in charge and his or her responsibility in the lockout/tagout.

(4) Simple Lockout/Tagout Procedure. All lockout/tagout procedures that involve only a qualified person(s) de-energizing one set of conductors or circuit part source for the sole purpose of safeguarding employees from exposure to electrical hazards shall be considered to be a simple lockout/tagout. Simple lockout/tagout procedures shall not be required to be written for each application. Each worker shall be responsible for his or her own lockout/tagout.

Exception: Lockout/tagout is not required for work on cord- and plug-connected equipment for which exposure to the hazards of unexpected energization of the equipment is controlled by the unplugging of the equipment from the energy source, provided that the plug is under the exclusive control of the employee performing the servicing and maintenance for the duration of the work.

(5) Complex Lockout/Tagout.
(a)   A complex lockout/tagout procedure shall be permitted where one or more of the following exists:

(1)   Multiple energy source
(2)   Multiple crews
(3)   Multiple crafts
(4)   Multiple locations
(5)   Multiple employers
(6)   Multiple disconnecting means
(7)   Particular sequences
(8)   Job or task that continues for more than one work period
   (b)   All complex lockout/tagout procedures shall require a written plan of execution that identifies the person in charge.
   (c)   The complex lockout/tagout procedure shall vest primary responsibility in an authorized employee for employees working under the protection of a group lockout or tagout device, such as an operation lock or lockbox. The person in charge shall be held accountable for safe execution of the complex lockout/tagout.
   (d)   Each authorized employee shall affix a personal lockout or tagout device to the group lockout device, group lockbox, or comparable mechanism when he or she begins work and shall remove those devices when he or she stops working on the machine or equipment being serviced or maintained.
   (e)   All complex lockout/tagout plans shall identify the method to account for all persons who might be exposed to electrical hazards in the course of the lockout/tagout.

(B) Elements of Control. The procedure shall identify elements of control.

(1) De-energizing Equipment (Shutdown). The procedure shall establish the person who performs the switching and where and how to de-energize the load.

(2) Stored Energy. The procedure shall include requirements for releasing stored electric or mechanical energy that might endanger personnel. All capacitors shall be discharged, and high-capacitance elements shall also be short-circuited and grounded before the associated equipment is touched or worked on. Springs shall be released or physical restraint shall be applied when necessary to immobilize mechanical equipment and pneumatic and hydraulic pressure reservoirs. Other sources of stored energy shall be blocked or otherwise relieved.

Informational Note: For more information on methods and procedures to place capacitors in an electrically safe work condition, see 360.3, 360.5, and Informative Annex R, Working with Capacitors.

(3) Disconnecting Means. The procedure shall identify how to verify that the circuit is de-energized (open).

(4) Responsibility. The procedure shall identify the person who is responsible for verifying that the lockout/tagout procedure is implemented and who is responsible for ensuring that the task is completed prior to removing locks/tags. A mechanism to accomplish lockout/tagout for multiple (complex) jobs/tasks where required, including the person responsible for coordination, shall be included.

(5) Verification. The procedure shall verify that equipment cannot be restarted. The equipment operating controls, such as push-buttons, selector switches, and electrical interlocks, shall be operated or otherwise it shall be verified that the equipment cannot be restarted.

(6) Testing. The procedure shall establish the following:

(1)   Test instrument to be used, the required PPE, and the person who will use it to verify proper operation of the test instrument on a known voltage source before and after use
(2)   Requirement to define the boundary of the electrically safe work condition
(3)   Requirement to test before touching every exposed conductor or circuit part(s) within the defined boundary of the work area
(4)   Requirement to retest for absence of voltage when circuit conditions change or when the job location has been left unattended
(5)   Planning considerations that include methods of verification where there is no accessible exposed point to take voltage measurements

(7) Grounding. Grounding requirements for the circuit shall be established, including whether the temporary protective grounding equipment shall be installed for the duration of the task or is temporarily established by the procedure. Grounding needs or requirements shall be permitted to be covered in other work rules and might not be part of the lockout/tagout procedure.

(8) Shift Change. A method shall be identified in the procedure to transfer responsibility for lockout/tagout to another person or to the person in charge when the job or task extends beyond one shift.

(9) Coordination. The procedure shall establish how coordination is accomplished with other jobs or tasks in progress, including related jobs or tasks at remote locations as well as the person responsible for coordination.

(10) Accountability for Personnel. A method shall be identified in the procedure to account for all persons who could be exposed to hazardous energy during the lockout/tagout.

(11) Lockout/Tagout Application. The procedure shall clearly identify when and where lockout applies, in addition to when and where tagout applies, and shall address the following:

(1)   Lockout shall be defined as installing a lockout device on all sources of hazardous energy such that operation of the disconnecting means is prohibited, and forcible removal of the lock is required to operate the disconnecting means.
(2)   Tagout shall be defined as installing a tagout device on all sources of hazardous energy, such that operation of the disconnecting means is prohibited. The tagout device shall be installed in the same position available for the lockout device.
(3)   Where it is not possible to attach a lock to existing disconnecting means, the disconnecting means shall not be used as the only means to put the circuit in an electrically safe work condition.

(4) The use of tagout procedures without a lock shall be permitted only in cases where equipment design precludes the installation of a lock on an energy isolation device(s). When tagout is employed, at least one additional safety measure shall be employed. In such cases, the procedure shall clearly establish responsibilities and accountability for each person who might be exposed to electrical hazards.

Informational Note: Examples of additional safety measures include the removal of an isolating circuit element such as fuses, blocking of the controlling switch, or opening an extra disconnecting device to reduce the likelihood of inadvertent energization.

(12) Removal of Lockout/Tagout Devices. The procedure shall identify the details for removing locks or tags when the installing individual is unavailable. When locks or tags are removed by someone other than the installer, the employer shall attempt to locate that person prior to removing the lock or tag. When the lock or tag is removed because the installer is unavailable, the installer shall be informed prior to returning to work.

(13) Release for Return to Service. The procedure shall identify steps to be taken when the job or task requiring lockout/tagout is completed. Before electric circuits or equipment are re-energized, tests and visual inspections shall be conducted to verify that all tools, mechanical restraints and electrical jumpers, short circuits, and temporary protective grounding equipment have been removed, so that the circuits and equipment are in a condition to be safely energized. When applicable, the employees responsible for operating the machines or process shall be notified when circuits and equipment are ready to be energized, and such employees shall provide assistance as necessary to safely energize the circuits and equipment. The procedure shall contain a statement requiring the area to be inspected to ensure that nonessential items have been removed. One such step shall ensure that all personnel are clear of exposure to dangerous conditions resulting from re-energizing the service and that blocked mechanical equipment or grounded equipment is cleared and prepared for return to service.

(14) Temporary Release for Testing/Positioning. The procedure shall clearly identify the steps and qualified persons' responsibilities when the job or task requiring lockout/tagout is to be interrupted temporarily for testing or positioning of equipment; then the steps shall be identical to the steps for return to service.

Informational Note: See 110.8 for requirements when using test instruments and equipment.

Δ **120.5 Process for Establishing and Verifying an Electrically Safe Work Condition.** Establishing and verifying an electrically safe work condition shall include all of the following steps, which shall be performed in the order presented, if feasible:

(1) Determine all possible sources of electrical supply to the specific equipment. Check applicable up-to-date drawings, diagrams, and identification tags.

(2) After properly interrupting the load current, open the disconnecting device(s) for each source.

(3) Wherever possible, visually verify that all blades of the disconnecting devices are fully open or that drawout-type circuit breakers are withdrawn to the test or fully disconnected position.

(4) Release stored electrical energy.

(5) Block or relieve stored nonelectrical energy in devices to the extent the circuit parts cannot be unintentionally energized by such devices.

(6) Apply lockout/tagout devices in accordance with a documented and established procedure.

(7) Use an adequately rated portable test instrument to test each phase conductor or circuit part to test for the absence of voltage. Test each phase conductor or circuit part both phase-to-phase and phase-to-ground. Before and after each test, determine that the test instrument is operating satisfactorily through verification on any known voltage source.

Exception No. 1 to 7: An adequately rated permanently mounted absence of voltage tester shall be permitted to be used to test for the absence of voltage of the conductors or circuit parts at the work location, provided it meets all of the following requirements: (1) It is permanently mounted and installed in accordance with the manufacturer's instructions and tests the conductors and circuit parts at the point of work; (2) It is listed and labeled for the purpose of testing for the absence of voltage; (3) It tests each phase conductor or circuit part both phase-to-phase and phase-to-ground; (4) The test device is verified as operating satisfactorily on any known voltage source before and after testing for the absence of voltage.

Exception No. 2 to 7: On electrical systems over 1000 volts, noncontact capacitive test instruments shall be permitted to be used to test each phase conductor.

Informational Note No. 1: See UL 61010-1, *Safety Requirements for Electrical Equipment for Measurement, Control, and Laboratory Use, Part 1: General Requirements,* for rating, overvoltage category, and design requirements for voltage measurement and test instruments intended for use on electrical systems 1000 volts and below.

Informational No. 2: For additional information on rating and design requirements for permanently mounted absence of voltage testers, refer to UL 1436, *Outlet Circuit Testers and Other Similar Indicating Devices.*

Informational Note No. 3: For additional information on rating and design requirements for voltage detectors, refer to IEC 61243-1, *Live Working — Voltage Detectors — Part 1: Capacitive type to be used for voltages exceeding 1kV a.c.,* or IEC 61243-2, *Live Working — Voltage Detectors — Part 2: Resistive type to be used for voltages of 1kV to 36 kV a.c.,* or IEC 61243-3, *Live Working — Voltage Detectors — Part 3: Two-pole low voltage type.*

(8) Where the possibility of induced voltages or stored electrical energy exists, ground all circuit conductors and circuit parts before touching them. Where it could be reasonably anticipated that the conductors or circuit parts being de-energized could contact other exposed energized conductors or circuit parts, apply temporary protective grounding equipment in accordance with the following:

a. *Placement.* Temporary protective grounding equipment shall be placed at such locations and arranged in such a manner as to prevent each employee from being exposed to a shock hazard (i.e., hazardous differences in electrical potential). The location, sizing, and application of temporary protective grounding equipment shall be identified as part of the employer's job planning.

b. *Capacity.* Temporary protective grounding equipment shall be capable of conducting the maximum fault current that could flow at the point of grounding for the time necessary to clear the fault.

Informational Note: ASTM F855, *Standard Specification for Temporary Protective Grounds to be Used on De-energized Electric Power Lines and Equipment*, is an example of a standard that contains information on capacity of temporary protective grounding equipment.

    c. *Impedance.* Temporary protective grounding equipment and connections shall have an impedance low enough to cause immediate operation of protective devices in case of unintentional energizing of the electric conductors or circuit parts.

ARTICLE 130
Work Involving Electrical Hazards

Δ **130.1 General.** Article 130 covers requirements for work involving electrical hazards such as the electrical safety-related work practices, assessments, precautions, and procedures when an electrically safe work condition cannot be established.

Safety-related work practices shall be used to safeguard employees from injury while they are exposed to electrical hazards from electrical conductors or circuit parts that are or can become energized.

When energized electrical conductors and circuit parts operating at voltages equal to or greater than 50 volts are not put into an electrically safe work condition, and work is performed as permitted in accordance with 110.4, all of the following requirements shall apply:

(1) Only qualified persons shall be permitted to work on electrical conductors or circuit parts that have not been put into an electrically safe work condition.
(2) An energized electrical work permit shall be completed as required by 130.2.
(3) A shock risk assessment shall be performed as required by 130.4.
(4) An arc flash risk assessment shall be performed as required by 130.5.

All requirements of Article 130 shall apply whether an incident energy analysis is completed or if Table 130.7(C)(15)(a), Table 130.7(C)(15)(b), and Table 130.7(C)(15)(c) are used in lieu of an incident energy analysis.

130.2 Energized Electrical Work Permit.

Δ **(A) When Required.** When work is performed as permitted in accordance with 110.4, an energized electrical work permit shall be required and documented under any of the following conditions:

(1) When work is performed within the restricted approach boundary
(2) When the employee interacts with the equipment when conductors or circuit parts are not exposed but an increased likelihood of injury from an exposure to an arc flash hazard exists

(B) Elements of Work Permit. The work permit shall include, but not be limited to, the following items:

(1) Description of the circuit and equipment to be worked on and their location
(2) Description of the work to be performed
(3) Justification for why the work must be performed in an energized condition *[see 110.4]*
(4) Description of the safe work practices to be employed *(see 130.1)*
(5) Results of the shock risk assessment *[see 130.4(A)]*
    a. Voltage to which personnel will be exposed
    b. Limited approach boundary *[see 130.4(F), Table 130.4(E)(a), and Table 130.4(E)(b)]*
    c. Restricted approach boundary *[see 130.4(G), Table 130.4(E)(a), and Table 130.4(E)(b)]*
    d. Personal and other protective equipment required by this standard to safely perform the assigned task and to protect against the shock hazard *[see 130.4(F), 130.7(C)(1) through (C)(16), and 130.7(D)]*
(6) Results of the arc flash risk assessment *[see 130.5]*
    a. Available incident energy at the working distance or arc flash PPE category *(see 130.5)*
    b. Personal and other protective equipment required by this standard to protect against the arc flash hazard *[see 130.5(F), 130.7(C)(1) through (C)(16), Table 130.7(C)(15)(c), and 130.7(D)]*
    c. Arc flash boundary *[see 130.5(E)]*
(7) Means employed to restrict the access of unqualified persons from the work area *[see 130.7(E)]*
(8) Evidence of completion of a job briefing, including a discussion of any job-specific hazards *[see 110.5(I)]*
(9) Energized work approval (authorizing or responsible management, safety officer, or owner, etc.) signature(s)

    Informational Note: For an example of an acceptable energized work permit, see Figure J.1.

Δ **(C) Exemptions to Work Permit.** Electrical work shall be permitted without an energized electrical work permit if a qualified person is provided with and uses appropriate safe work practices and PPE in accordance with Chapter 1 under any of the following conditions:

(1) Testing, troubleshooting, or voltage measuring
(2) Thermography, ultrasound, or visual inspections if the restricted approach boundary is not crossed
(3) Access to and egress from an area with energized electrical equipment if no electrical work is performed and the restricted approach boundary is not crossed
(4) General housekeeping and miscellaneous non-electrical tasks if the restricted approach boundary is not crossed

130.4 Shock Risk Assessment.

(A) General. A shock risk assessment shall be performed:

(1) To identify shock hazards
(2) To estimate the likelihood of occurrence of injury or damage to health and the potential severity of injury or damage to health
(3) To determine if additional protective measures are required, including the use of PPE

N **(B) Estimate of Likelihood and Severity.** The estimate of likelihood of occurrence of injury or damage to health and the potential severity of injury or damage to health shall take into consideration all of the following:

(1) The design of the electrical equipment

(2) The electrical equipment operating condition and the condition of maintenance

(C) Additional Protective Measures. If additional protective measures are required, they shall be selected and implemented according to the hierarchy of risk control identified in 110.5(H)(3). When the additional protective measures include the use of PPE, the following shall be determined:

(1) The voltage to which personnel will be exposed
(2) The boundary requirements
(3) The personal and other protective equipment required by this standard to protect against the shock hazard

(D) Documentation. The results of the shock risk assessment shall be documented.

(E) Shock Protection Boundaries. The shock protection boundaries identified as limited approach boundary and restricted approach boundary shall be applicable where personnel are approaching exposed energized electrical conductors or circuit parts. Table 130.4(E)(a) shall be used for the distances associated with various ac system voltages. Table 130.4(E)(b) shall be used for the distances associated with various dc system voltages.

Informational Note: In certain instances, the arc flash boundary might be a greater distance from the energized electrical conductors or circuit parts than the limited approach boundary. The shock protection boundaries and the arc flash boundary are independent of each other.

(F) Limited Approach Boundary.

(1) Approach by Unqualified Persons. Unless permitted by 130.4(F)(3), no unqualified person shall be permitted to approach nearer than the limited approach boundary of energized conductors and circuit parts.

(2) Working at or Close to the Limited Approach Boundary. Where one or more unqualified persons are working at or close to the limited approach boundary, the alerting methods in 130.7(E) shall be applied to advise the unqualified person(s) of the electrical hazard and warn him or her to stay outside of the limited approach boundary.

(3) Entering the Limited Approach Boundary. Where there is a need for an unqualified person(s) to cross the limited approach boundary, a qualified person shall advise the unqualified person(s) of the possible hazards and continuously escort the unqualified person(s) while inside the limited approach boundary. Under no circumstance shall unqualified person(s) be permitted to cross the restricted approach boundary.

(G) Restricted Approach Boundary. No qualified person shall approach or take any conductive object closer to exposed energized electrical conductors or circuit parts than the restricted approach boundary set forth in Table 130.4(E)(a) and Table 130.4(E)(b), unless one of the following conditions applies:

(1) The qualified person is insulated or guarded from energized electrical conductors or circuit parts operating at 50 volts or more. Insulating gloves and sleeves are considered insulation only with regard to the energized parts upon which work is performed.
(2) The energized electrical conductors or circuit parts are insulated from the qualified person and from any other conductive object at a different potential.

Δ **Table 130.4(E)(a) Shock Protection Approach Boundaries to Exposed Energized Electrical Conductors or Circuit Parts for Alternating-Current Systems**

(1)	(2)	(3)	(4)
	Limited Approach Boundary[b]		
Nominal System Voltage Range, Phase to Phase[a]	Exposed Movable Conductor[c]	Exposed Fixed Circuit Part	Restricted Approach Boundary[b]; Includes Inadvertent Movement Adder
Less than 50 V	Not specified	Not specified	Not specified
50 V–150 V[d]	3.0 m (10 ft 0 in.)	1.0 m (3 ft 6 in.)	Avoid contact
151 V–750 V	3.0 m (10 ft 0 in.)	1.0 m (3 ft 6 in.)	0.3 m (1 ft 0 in.)
751 V–15 kV	3.0 m (10 ft 0 in.)	1.5 m (5 ft 0 in.)	0.7 m (2 ft 2 in.)
15.1 kV–36 kV	3.0 m (10 ft 0 in.)	1.8 m (6 ft 0 in.)	0.8 m (2 ft 9 in.)
36.1 kV–46 kV	3.0 m (10 ft 0 in.)	2.5 m (8 ft 0 in.)	0.8 m (2 ft 9 in.)
46.1 kV–72.5 kV	3.0 m (10 ft 0 in.)	2.5 m (8 ft 0 in.)	1.0 m (3 ft 6 in.)
72.6 kV–121 kV	3.3 m (10 ft 8 in.)	2.5 m (8 ft 0 in.)	1.0 m (3 ft 6 in.)
138 kV–145 kV	3.4 m (11 ft 0 in.)	3.0 m (10 ft 0 in.)	1.2 m (3 ft 10 in.)
161 kV–169 kV	3.6 m (11 ft 8 in.)	3.6 m (11 ft 8 in.)	1.3 m (4 ft 3 in.)
230 kV–242 kV	4.0 m (13 ft 0 in.)	4.0 m (13 ft 0 in.)	1.7 m (5 ft 8 in.)
345 kV–362 kV	4.7 m (15 ft 4 in.)	4.7 m (15 ft 4 in.)	2.8 m (9 ft 2 in.)
500 kV–550 kV	5.8 m (19 ft 0 in.)	5.8 m (19 ft 0 in.)	3.6 m (11 ft 8 in.)
765 kV–800 kV	7.2 m (23 ft 9 in.)	7.2 m (23 ft 9 in.)	4.9 m (15 ft 11 in.)

Notes:
(1) For arc flash boundary, see 130.5(E).
(2) All dimensions are distance from exposed energized electrical conductors or circuit part to employee.
[a]For single-phase systems above 250 volts, select the range that is equal to the system's maximum phase-to-ground voltage multiplied by 1.732.
[b]See definition in Article 100 and text in 130.4(D)(2) and Informative Annex C for elaboration.
[c]*Exposed movable conductors* describes a condition in which the distance between the conductor and a person is not under the control of the person. The term is normally applied to overhead line conductors supported by poles.
[d]This includes circuits where the exposure does not exceed 120 volts nominal.

Table 130.4(E)(b) Shock Protection Approach Boundaries to Exposed Energized Electrical Conductors or Circuit Parts for Direct-Current Voltage Systems

(1)	(2)		(3)	(4)
	Limited Approach Boundary			**Restricted Approach Boundary; Includes Inadvertent Movement Adder**
Nominal Potential Difference	**Exposed Movable Conductor***	**Exposed Fixed Circuit Part**		
Less than 50 V	Not specified	Not specified		Not specified
50 V–300 V	3.0 m (10 ft 0 in.)	1.0 m (3 ft 6 in.)		Avoid contact
301 V–1 kV	3.0 m (10 ft 0 in.)	1.0 m (3 ft 6 in.)		0.3 m (1 ft 0 in.)
1.1 kV–5 kV	3.0 m (10 ft 0 in.)	1.5 m (5 ft 0 in.)		0.5 m (1 ft 5 in.)
5 kV–15 kV	3.0 m (10 ft 0 in.)	1.5 m (5 ft 0 in.)		0.7 m (2 ft 2 in.)
15.1 kV–45 kV	3.0 m (10 ft 0 in.)	2.5 m (8 ft 0 in.)		0.8 m (2 ft 9 in.)
45.1 kV– 75 kV	3.0 m (10 ft 0 in.)	2.5 m (8 ft 0 in.)		1.0 m (3 ft 6 in.)
75.1 kV–150 kV	3.3 m (10 ft 8 in.)	3.0 m (10 ft 0 in.)		1.2 m (3 ft 10 in.)
150.1 kV–250 kV	3.6 m (11 ft 8 in.)	3.6 m (11 ft 8 in.)		1.6 m (5 ft 3 in.)
250.1 kV–500 kV	6.0 m (20 ft 0 in.)	6.0 m (20 ft 0 in.)		3.5 m (11 ft 6 in.)
500.1 kV–800 kV	8.0 m (26 ft 0 in.)	8.0 m (26 ft 0 in.)		5.0 m (16 ft 5 in.)

Note: All dimensions are distance from exposed energized electrical conductors or circuit parts to worker.

**Exposed movable conductor* describes a condition in which the distance between the conductor and a person is not under the control of the person. The term is normally applied to overhead line conductors supported by poles.

130.5 Arc Flash Risk Assessment.

(A) General. An arc flash risk assessment shall be performed:

(1) To identify arc flash hazards
(2) To estimate the likelihood of occurrence of injury or damage to health and the potential severity of injury or damage to health
(3) To determine if additional protective measures are required, including the use of PPE

(B) Estimate of Likelihood and Severity. The estimate of the likelihood of occurrence of injury or damage to health and the potential severity of injury or damage to health shall take into consideration the following:

(1) The design of the electrical equipment, including its overcurrent protective device and its operating time
(2) The electrical equipment operating condition and condition of maintenance

Δ **(C) Additional Protective Measures.** If additional protective measures are required they shall be selected and implemented according to the hierarchy of risk control identified in 110.5(H)(3). When the additional protective measures include the use of PPE, the following shall be determined:

(1) Appropriate safety-related work practices
(2) The arc flash boundary
(3) The PPE to be used within the arc flash boundary

Table 130.5(C) shall be permitted to be used to estimate the likelihood of occurrence of an arc flash event to determine if additional protective measures are required.

(D) Documentation. The results of the arc flash risk assessment shall be documented.

(E) Arc Flash Boundary.

(1) The arc flash boundary shall be the distance at which the incident energy equals 1.2 cal/cm^2 (5 J/cm^2).

> Informational Note: For information on estimating the arc flash boundary, see Informative Annex D.

(2) The arc flash boundary shall be permitted to be determined by Table 130.7(C)(15)(a) or Table 130.7(C)(15)(b) when the requirements of these tables apply.

(F) Arc Flash PPE. One of the following methods shall be used for the selection of arc flash PPE:

(1) The incident energy analysis method in accordance with 130.5(G)
(2) The arc flash PPE category method in accordance with 130.7(C)(15)

Either, but not both, methods shall be permitted to be used on the same piece of equipment. The results of an incident energy analysis to specify an arc flash PPE category in Table 130.7(C)(15)(c) shall not be permitted.

(G) Incident Energy Analysis Method. The incident energy exposure level shall be based on the working distance of the employee's face and chest areas from a prospective arc source for the specific task to be performed. Arc-rated clothing and other PPE shall be used by the employee based on the incident energy exposure associated with the specific task. Recognizing that incident energy increases as the distance from the arc flash decreases, additional PPE shall be used for any parts of the body that are closer than the working distance at which the incident energy was determined.

The incident energy analysis shall take into consideration the characteristics of the overcurrent protective device and its fault clearing time, including its condition of maintenance.

The incident energy analysis shall be updated when changes occur in the electrical distribution system that could affect the results of the analysis. The incident energy analysis shall also be reviewed for accuracy at intervals not to exceed 5 years.

Table 130.5(G) identifies the arc-rated clothing and other PPE requirements of Article 130 and shall be permitted to be used with the incident energy analysis method of selecting arc flash PPE.

> Informational Note: For information on estimating the incident energy, see Informative Annex D. For information on selection of arc-rated clothing and other PPE, see Informative Annex H.

Shaded text = Revisions.   Δ = Text deletions and figure/table revisions.   • = Section deletions.   *N* = New material.

Δ **Table 130.5(C) Estimate of the Likelihood of Occurrence of an Arc Flash Incident for ac and dc Systems**

Task	Equipment Condition[a]	Likelihood of Occurrence[b]
Reading a panel meter while operating a meter switch. Performing infrared thermography and other non-contact inspections outside the restricted approach boundary. This activity does not include opening of doors or covers. Working on control circuits with exposed energized electrical conductors and circuit parts, nominal 125 volts ac or dc, or below without any other exposed energized equipment over nominal 125 volts ac or dc, including opening of hinged covers to gain access. Examination of insulated cable with no manipulation of cable. For dc systems, maintenance on a single cell of a battery system or multi-cell units in an open rack.	Any	No
For ac systems, work on energized electrical conductors and circuit parts, including electrical testing. Operation of a CB or switch the first time after installation or completion of maintenance in the equipment. For dc systems, working on energized electrical conductors and circuit parts of series-connected battery cells, including electrical testing. Removal or installation of CBs or switches. Opening hinged door(s) or cover(s) or removal of bolted covers (to expose bare, energized electrical conductors and circuit parts). For dc systems, this includes bolted covers, such as battery terminal covers. Application of temporary protective grounding equipment, after voltage test. Working on control circuits with exposed energized electrical conductors and circuit parts, greater than 120 volts. Insertion or removal of individual starter buckets from motor control center (MCC). Insertion or removal (racking) of circuit breakers (CBs) or starters from cubicles, doors open or closed. Insertion or removal of plug-in devices into or from busways. Examination of insulated cable with manipulation of cable. Working on exposed energized electrical conductors and circuit parts of equipment directly supplied by a panelboard or motor control center. Insertion or removal of revenue meters (kW-hour, at primary voltage and current). Insertion or removal of covers for battery intercell connector(s). For dc systems, working on exposed energized electrical conductors and circuit parts of utilization equipment directly supplied by a dc source. Opening voltage transformer or control power transformer compartments. Operation of outdoor disconnect switch (hookstick operated) at 1 kV through 15 kV. Operation of outdoor disconnect switch (gang-operated, from grade) at 1 kV through 15 kV.	Any	Yes
Operation of a CB, switch, contactor, or starter. Voltage testing on individual battery cells or individual multi-cell units. Removal or installation of covers for equipment such as wireways, junction boxes, and cable trays that does not expose bare, energized electrical conductors and circuit parts. Opening a panelboard hinged door or cover to access dead front overcurrent devices. Removal of battery nonconductive intercell connector covers.	Normal	No

(continues)

Δ **Table 130.5(C)**   *Continued*

Task	Equipment Condition[a]	Likelihood of Occurrence[b]
Maintenance and testing on individual battery cells or individual multi-cell units in an open rack	Abnormal	Yes
Insertion or removal of individual cells or multi-cell units of a battery system in an open rack.		
Arc-resistant equipment with the DOORS CLOSED and SECURED, and where the available fault current and fault clearing time does not exceed that of the arc-resistant rating of the equipment in one of the following conditions:		
(1) Insertion or removal of individual starter buckets		
(2) Insertion or removal (racking) of CBs from cubicles		
(3) Insertion or removal (racking) of ground and test device		
(4) Insertion or removal (racking) of voltage transformers on or off the bus		

[a]Equipment is considered to be in a "normal operating condition" if all of the conditions in 110.4(D) are satisfied.

[b]As defined in this standard, the two components of risk are the likelihood of occurrence of injury or damage to health and the severity of injury or damage to health that results from a hazard. Risk assessment is an overall process that involves estimating both the likelihood of occurrence and severity to determine if additional protective measures are required. The estimate of the likelihood of occurrence contained in this table does not cover every possible condition or situation, nor does it address severity of injury or damage to health. Where this table identifies "No" as an estimate of likelihood of occurrence, it means that an arc flash incident is not likely to occur. Where this table identifies "Yes" as an estimate of likelihood of occurrence, it means an arc flash incident should be considered likely to occur. The likelihood of occurrence must be combined with the potential severity of the arcing incident to determine if additional protective measures are required to be selected and implemented according to the hierarchy of risk control identified in 110.5(H)(3).

Informational Note No. 1: An example of a standard that provides information for arc-resistant equipment referred to in Table 130.5(C) is IEEE C37.20.7, *Guide for Testing Switchgear Rated Up to 52 kV for Internal Arcing Faults.*

Informational Note No. 2: Improper or inadequate maintenance can result in increased fault clearing time of the overcurrent protective device, thus increasing the incident energy. Where equipment is not properly installed or maintained, PPE selection based on incident energy analysis or the PPE category method might not provide adequate protection from arc flash hazards.

Informational Note No. 3: Both larger and smaller available fault currents could result in higher incident energy. If the available fault current increases without a decrease in the fault clearing time of the overcurrent protective device, the incident energy will increase. If the available fault current decreases, resulting in a longer fault clearing time for the overcurrent protective device, incident energy could also increase.

Informational Note No. 4: The occurrence of an arcing fault inside an enclosure produces a variety of physical phenomena very different from a bolted fault. For example, the arc energy resulting from an arc developed in the air will cause a sudden pressure increase and localized overheating. Equipment and design practices are available to minimize the energy levels and the number of procedures that could expose an employee to high levels of incident energy. Proven designs such as arc-resistant switchgear, remote racking (insertion or removal), remote opening and closing of switching devices, high-resistance grounding of low-voltage and 5000-volt (nominal) systems, current limitation, and specification of covered bus or covered conductors within equipment are available to reduce the risk associated with an arc flash incident. See Informative Annex O for safety-related design requirements.

Informational Note No. 5: For additional direction for performing maintenance on overcurrent protective devices, see Chapter 2, Safety-Related Maintenance Requirements.

Informational Note No. 6: See IEEE 1584, *Guide for Performing Arc Flash Hazard Calculations,* for more information regarding incident energy and the arc flash boundary for three-phase systems.

Δ **Table 130.5(G) Selection of Arc-Rated Clothing and Other PPE When the Incident Energy Analysis Method Is Used**

Incident energy exposures equal to 1.2 cal/cm² up to and including 12 cal/cm²
Arc-rated clothing with an arc rating equal to or greater than the estimated incident energy[a]
Arc-rated long-sleeve shirt and pants or arc-rated coverall or arc flash suit (SR)
Arc-rated face shield and arc-rated balaclava or arc flash suit hood (SR)[b]
Arc-rated outerwear (e.g., jacket, parka, rainwear, hard hat liner, high-visibility apparel) (AN)[e]
Heavy-duty leather gloves, arc-rated gloves, or rubber insulating gloves with leather protectors (SR)[c]
Hard hat
Safety glasses or safety goggles (SR)
Hearing protection
Leather footwear[d]

Incident energy exposures greater than 12 cal/cm²
Arc-rated clothing with an arc rating equal to or greater than the estimated incident energy[a]
Arc-rated long-sleeve shirt and pants or arc-rated coverall or arc flash suit (SR)
Arc-rated arc flash suit hood
Arc-rated outerwear (e.g., jacket, parka, rainwear, hard hat liner, high-visibility apparel) (AN)[e]
Arc-rated gloves or rubber insulating gloves with leather protectors (SR)[c]
Hard hat
Safety glasses or safety goggles (SR)
Hearing protection
Leather footwear[d]

SR: Selection of one in group is required.
AN: As needed.
[a]Arc ratings can be for a single layer, such as an arc-rated shirt and pants or a coverall, or for an arc flash suit or a multi-layer system if tested as a combination consisting of an arc-rated shirt and pants, coverall, and arc flash suit.
[b]Face shields with a wrap-around guarding to protect the face, chin, forehead, ears, and neck area are required by 130.7(C)(10)(c). Where the back of the head is inside the arc flash boundary, a balaclava or an arc flash hood shall be required for full head and neck protection.
[c]Rubber insulating gloves with leather protectors provide arc flash protection in addition to shock protection. Higher class rubber insulating gloves with leather protectors, due to their increased material thickness, provide increased arc flash protection.
[d]Footwear other than leather or dielectric shall be permitted to be used provided it has been tested to demonstrate no ignition, melting, or dripping at the estimated incident energy exposure.
[e]The arc rating of outer layers worn over arc-rated clothing as protection from the elements or for other safety purposes, and that are not used as part of a layered system, shall not be required to be equal to or greater than the estimated incident energy exposure.

(H) Equipment Labeling. Electrical equipment such as switchboards, panelboards, industrial control panels, meter socket enclosures, and motor control centers that are in other than dwelling units and that are likely to require examination, adjustment, servicing, or maintenance while energized shall be marked with a label containing all the following information:

(1) Nominal system voltage
(2) Arc flash boundary
(3) At least one of the following:

   a. Available incident energy and the corresponding working distance, or the arc flash PPE category in Table 130.7(C)(15)(a) or Table 130.7(C)(15)(b) for the equipment, but not both
   b. Minimum arc rating of clothing
   c. Site-specific level of PPE

Exception No. 1: Unless changes in electrical distribution system(s) render the label inaccurate, labels applied prior to the effective date of this edition of the standard shall be acceptable if they complied with the requirements for equipment labeling in the standard in effect at the time the labels were applied.

Exception No. 2: In supervised industrial installations where conditions of maintenance and engineering supervision ensure that only qualified persons monitor and service the system, the information required in 130.5(H)(1) through 130.5(H)(3) shall be permitted to be documented in a manner that is readily available to persons likely to perform examination, servicing, maintenance, and operation of the equipment while energized.

The method of calculating and the data to support the information for the label shall be documented. The data shall be reviewed for accuracy at intervals not to exceed 5 years. Where the review of the data identifies a change that renders the label inaccurate, the label shall be updated.

The owner of the electrical equipment shall be responsible for the documentation, installation, and maintenance of the marked label.

130.7 Personal and Other Protective Equipment.

(A) General. Employees exposed to electrical hazards when the risk associated with that hazard is not adequately reduced by the applicable electrical installation requirements shall be provided with, and shall use, protective equipment that is designed and constructed for the specific part of the body to be protected and for the work to be performed.

Informational Note: The PPE requirements of 130.7 are intended to protect a person from arc flash and shock hazards. While some situations could result in burns to the skin, even with the protection selected, burn injury should be reduced and survivable. Due to the explosive effect of some arc events, physical trauma injuries could occur. The PPE requirements of 130.7 do not address protection against physical trauma other than exposure to the thermal effects of an arc flash.

(B) Care of Equipment. Protective equipment shall be maintained in a safe, clean, and reliable condition and in accordance with manufacturers' instructions. The protective equipment shall be visually inspected before each use. Protective equipment shall be stored in a manner to prevent damage from physically damaging conditions and from moisture, dust, or other deteriorating agents.

Informational Note: Specific requirements for periodic testing of electrical protective equipment are given in 130.7(C)(14) and 130.7(G).

(C) Personal Protective Equipment (PPE).

(1) General. When an employee is working within the restricted approach boundary, the worker shall wear PPE in accordance with 130.4. When an employee is working within the arc flash boundary, he or she shall wear protective clothing and other PPE in accordance with 130.5. All parts of the body inside the arc flash boundary shall be protected.

Informational Note: Where the estimated incident energy exposure is greater than the arc rating of commercially available arc-rated PPE, then for the purpose of testing for the absence of voltage, the following examples of risk reduction methods could be used to reduce the likelihood of occurrence of an arcing event or the severity of exposure:

(1) Use noncontact proximity test instrument(s) or measurement of voltage on the secondary side of a low-voltage transformer (VT) mounted in the equipment before using a contact test instrument to test for the absence of voltage below 1000 volts.
(2) If equipment design allows, observe visible gaps between the equipment conductors and circuit parts and the electrical source(s) of supply.
(3) Increase the working distance.
(4) Consider system design options to reduce the incident energy level.

(2) Movement and Visibility. When arc-rated clothing is worn to protect an employee, it shall cover all ignitible clothing and shall allow for movement and visibility.

(3) Head, Face, Neck, and Chin (Head Area) Protection. Employees shall wear nonconductive head protection wherever there is a danger of head injury from electric shock or burns due to contact with energized electrical conductors or circuit parts or from flying objects resulting from electrical explosion. Employees shall wear nonconductive protective equipment for the face, neck, and chin whenever there is a danger of injury from exposure to electric arcs or flashes or from flying objects resulting from electrical explosion. If employees use hairnets or beard nets, or both, these items shall be arc rated.

Informational Note: See 130.7(C)(10)(b) and (C)(10)(c) for arc flash protective requirements.

(4) Eye Protection. Employees shall wear protective equipment for the eyes whenever there is danger of injury from electric arcs, flashes, or from flying objects resulting from electrical explosion.

(5) Hearing Protection. Employees shall wear hearing protection whenever working within the arc flash boundary.

(6) Body Protection. Employees shall wear arc-rated clothing wherever there is possible exposure to an electric arc flash above the threshold incident energy level for a second degree burn [1.2 cal/cm^2 (5 J/cm^2)].

(7) Hand and Arm Protection. Hand and arm protection shall be provided in accordance with 130.7(C)(7)(a), (C)(7)(b), and (C)(7)(c).

(a) *Shock Protection.* Employees shall wear rubber insulating gloves with leather protectors where there is a danger of hand injury from electric shock due to contact with exposed energized electrical conductors or circuit parts. Employees shall wear rubber insulating gloves with leather protectors and rubber insulating sleeves where there is a danger of hand and arm injury from electric shock due to contact with exposed energized electrical conductors or circuit parts. Rubber insulating gloves shall be rated for the voltage for which the gloves will be exposed. Rubber insulating gloves shall be permitted to be used without leather protectors, under the following conditions:

(1) There shall be no activity performed that risks cutting or damaging the glove.
(2) The rubber insulating gloves shall be electrically retested before reuse.
(3) The voltage rating of the rubber insulating gloves shall be reduced by 50 percent for class 00 and by one whole class for classes 0 through 4.

(b) *Arc Flash Protection.* Hand and arm protection shall be worn where there is possible exposure to arc flash burn. The apparel described in 130.7(C)(10)(d) shall be required for protection of hands from burns. Arm protection shall be accomplished by the apparel described in 130.7(C)(6).

(c) *Maintenance and Use.* Electrical protective equipment shall be maintained in a safe, reliable condition. Insulating equipment shall be inspected for damage before each day's use and immediately following any incident that can reasonably be suspected of having caused damage. Insulating gloves shall be given an air test, along with the inspection. Maximum use voltages for rubber insulating gloves shall not exceed that specified in Table 130.7(C)(7)(a). The top of the cuff of the protector glove shall be shorter than the rolled top of the cuff of the insulating glove by at least the distance specified in Table 130.7(C)(7)(a).

(d) *Periodic Electrical Tests.* Rubber insulating equipment shall be subjected to periodic electrical tests. Test voltages shall be in accordance with applicable state, federal, or local codes and standards. The maximum intervals between tests shall not exceed that specified in Table 130.7(C)(7)(b).

Informational Note: See OSHA 29 CFR 1910.137; ASTM F478, *Standard Specification for In-Service Care of Insulating Line Hose and Covers*; ASTM F479, *Standard Specification for In-Service Care of Insulating Blankets*; and ASTM F496, *Standard Specification for In-Service Care of Insulating Gloves and Sleeves*, which contain information related to in-service and testing requirements for rubber insulating equipment.

N **Table 130.7(C)(7)(a) Maximum Use Voltage for Rubber Insulating Gloves**

Class Designation of Glove or Sleeve	Maximum ac Use Voltage rms, volts	Maximum dc Use Voltage avg, volts	Distances Between Gauntlet and Cuff, minimum
00	500	750	13 mm (0.5 in.)
0	1,000	1,500	13 mm (0.5 in.)
1	7,500	11,250	25 mm (1 in.)
2	17,000	25,500	51 mm (2 in.)
3	26,500	39,750	76 mm (3 in.)
4	36,000	54,000	102 mm (4 in.)

(8) Foot Protection. Where insulated footwear is used as protection against step and touch potential, dielectric footwear shall be required. Insulated soles shall not be used as primary electrical protection.

Informational Note: Electrical Hazard footwear meeting ASTM F2413, *Standard Specification for Performance Requirements for Protective (Safety) Toe Cap Footwear*, can provide a secondary source of electric shock protection under dry conditions.

(9) Factors in Selection of Protective Clothing. Clothing and equipment that provide worker protection from shock and arc flash hazards shall be used. If arc-rated clothing is required, it shall cover associated parts of the body as well as all flammable apparel while allowing movement and visibility.

Clothing and equipment required for the degree of exposure shall be permitted to be worn alone or integrated with flammable, nonmelting apparel. Garments that are not arc rated shall not be permitted to be used to increase the arc rating of a garment or of a clothing system.

Informational Note: Protective clothing includes shirts, pants, coveralls, jackets, and parkas worn routinely by workers who, under normal working conditions, are exposed to momentary electric arc and related thermal hazards. Arc-rated rainwear worn in inclement weather is included in this category of clothing.

(a) *Layering.* Nonmelting, flammable fiber garments shall be permitted to be used as underlayers in conjunction with arc-rated garments in a layered system. If nonmelting, flammable fiber garments are used as underlayers, the system arc rating shall be sufficient to prevent breakopen of the innermost arc-rated layer at the expected arc exposure incident energy level to prevent ignition of flammable underlayers. Garments that are not arc rated shall not be permitted to be used to increase the arc rating of a garment or of a clothing system.

Informational Note: A typical layering system might include cotton underwear, a cotton shirt and trouser, and an arc-rated coverall. Specific tasks might call for additional arc-rated layers to achieve the required protection level.

(b) *Outer Layers.* Garments worn as outer layers over arc-rated clothing, such as jackets, high-visibility apparel, or rainwear, shall also be made from arc-rated material. The arc rating of outer layers worn over arc-rated clothing as protection from the elements or for other safety purposes, and that are not used as part of a layered system, shall not be required to be equal to or greater than the estimated incident energy exposure.

(c) *Underlayers.* Meltable fibers such as acetate, nylon, polyester, polypropylene, and spandex shall not be permitted in fabric underlayers.

Table 130.7(C)(7)(b) Rubber Insulating Equipment, Maximum Test Intervals

Rubber Insulating Equipment	When to Test
Blankets	Before first issue; every 12 months thereafter*
Covers	If insulating value is suspect
Gloves	Before first issue; every 6 months thereafter*
Line hose	If insulating value is suspect
Sleeves	Before first issue; every 12 months thereafter*

*New insulating equipment is not permitted to be placed into service unless it has been electrically tested within the previous 12 months. Insulating equipment that has been issued for service is not new and is required to be retested in accordance with the intervals in this table.

Exception: An incidental amount of elastic used on nonmelting fabric underwear or socks shall be permitted.

Informational Note No. 1: Arc-rated garments (e.g., shirts, trousers, and coveralls) worn as underlayers that neither ignite nor melt and drip in the course of an exposure to electric arc and related thermal hazards generally provide a higher system arc rating than nonmelting, flammable fiber underlayers.

Informational Note No. 2: Arc-rated underwear or undergarments used as underlayers generally provide a higher system arc rating than nonmelting, flammable fiber underwear or undergarments used as underlayers.

(d) *Coverage.* Clothing shall cover potentially exposed areas as completely as possible. Shirt and coverall sleeves shall be fastened at the wrists, shirts shall be tucked into pants, and shirts, coveralls, and jackets shall be closed at the neck.

(e) *Fit.* Tight-fitting clothing shall be avoided. Loose-fitting clothing provides additional thermal insulation because of air spaces. Arc-rated apparel shall fit properly such that it does not interfere with the work task.

(f) *Interference.* The garment selected shall result in the least interference with the task but still provide the necessary protection. The work method, location, and task could influence the protective equipment selected.

(10) Arc Flash Protective Equipment.

(a) *Arc Flash Suits.* Arc flash suit design shall permit easy and rapid removal by the wearer. The entire arc flash suit, including the hood's face shield, shall have an arc rating that is suitable for the arc flash exposure. When exterior air is supplied into the hood, the air hoses and pump housing shall be either covered by arc-rated materials or constructed of nonmelting and nonflammable materials.

(b) *Head Protection.*

(1) An arc-rated hood or an arc-rated balaclava with an arc-rated face shield shall be used when the back of the head is within the arc flash boundary.

(2) An arc-rated hood shall be used when the anticipated incident energy exposure exceeds 12 cal/cm^2 (50.2 J/cm^2).

(c) *Face Protection.* Face shields shall have an arc rating suitable for the arc flash exposure. Face shields with a wrap-around guarding to protect the face, chin, forehead, ears, and neck area shall be used. Face shields without an arc rating shall not be used. Eye protection (safety glasses or goggles) shall always be worn under face shields or hoods.

Informational Note: Face shields made with energy-absorbing formulations that can provide higher levels of protection from the radiant energy of an arc flash are available, but these shields are tinted and can reduce visual acuity and color perception. Additional illumination of the task area might be necessary when these types of arc-protective face shields are used.

(d) *Hand Protection.*

(1) Heavy-duty leather gloves or arc-rated gloves shall be worn where required for arc flash protection.

Informational Note: Heavy-duty leather gloves are made entirely of leather with minimum thickness of 0.03 in. (0.7 mm) and are unlined or lined with nonflammable, nonmelting fabrics. Heavy-duty leather gloves meeting this requirement have been shown to have ATPV values in excess of 10 cal/cm^2 (41.9 J/cm^2).

(2) Where insulating rubber gloves are used for shock protection, leather protectors shall be worn over the rubber gloves.

Informational Note: The leather protectors worn over rubber insulating gloves provide additional arc flash protection for the hands for arc flash protection exposure.

(e) *Foot Protection.* Leather footwear or dielectric footwear or both provide some arc flash protection to the feet and shall be used in all exposures greater than 4 cal/cm^2 (16.75 J/cm^2). Footwear other than leather or dielectric shall be permitted to be used provided it has been tested to demonstrate no ignition, melting, or dripping at the estimated incident energy exposure or the minimum arc rating for the respective arc flash PPE category.

(11) Clothing Material Characteristics. Arc-rated clothing shall meet the requirements described in 130.7(C)(12) and 130.7(C)(14).

Informational Note No. 1: Arc-rated materials, such as flame-retardant-treated cotton, meta-aramid, para-aramid, and poly-benzimidazole (PBI) fibers, provide thermal protection. These materials can ignite but will not continue to burn after the ignition source is removed. Arc-rated fabrics can reduce burn injuries during an arc flash exposure by providing a thermal barrier between the arc flash and the wearer.

Informational Note No. 2: Non-arc-rated cotton, polyester-cotton blends, nylon, nylon-cotton blends, silk, rayon, and wool fabrics are flammable. Fabrics, zipper tapes, and findings made of these materials can ignite and continue to burn on the body, resulting in serious burn injuries.

Informational Note No. 3: Rayon is a cellulose-based (wood pulp) synthetic fiber that is a flammable but nonmelting material.

Clothing consisting of fabrics, zipper tapes, and findings made from flammable synthetic materials that melt at temperatures below 315°C (600°F), such as acetate, acrylic, nylon, polyester, polyethylene, polypropylene, and spandex, either alone or in blends, shall not be used.

Informational Note: These materials melt as a result of arc flash exposure conditions, form intimate contact with the skin, and aggravate the burn injury.

Exception: Fiber blends that contain materials that melt, such as acetate, acrylic, nylon, polyester, polyethylene, polypropylene, and spandex, shall be permitted if such blends in fabrics are arc rated and do not exhibit evidence of melting and dripping during arc testing.

Informational Note: ASTM F1959/F1959M, *Standard Test Method for Determining the Arc Rating of Materials for Clothing*, and ASTM F1506, *Standard Performance Specification for Flame Resistant and Electric Arc Rated Protective Clothing Worn by Workers Exposed to Flames and Electric Arcs*, contain information on test methods used to determine the arc rating of fabrics.

(12) Clothing and Other Apparel Not Permitted. Clothing and other apparel (such as hard hat liners and hair nets) made from materials that do not meet the requirements of 130.7(C)(11) regarding melting or made from materials that do not meet the flammability requirements shall not be permitted to be worn.

Informational Note: Some flame-resistant fabrics, such as non-flame-resistant modacrylic and nondurable flame-retardant treatments of cotton, are not recommended for industrial electrical or utility applications.

Exception No. 1: Nonmelting, flammable (non-arc-rated) materials shall be permitted to be used as underlayers to arc-rated clothing, as described in 130.7(C)(11).

Exception No. 2: Where the work to be performed inside the arc flash boundary exposes the worker to multiple hazards, such as airborne contaminants, and the risk assessment identifies that the level of protection is adequate to address the arc flash hazard, non-arc-rated PPE shall be permitted.

Δ **(13) Care and Maintenance of Arc-Rated Clothing and Arc-Rated Arc Flash Suits.**

(a) *Inspection.* Arc-rated apparel shall be inspected before each use. Work clothing or arc flash suits that are contaminated or damaged to the extent that their protective qualities are impaired shall not be used. Protective items that become contaminated with grease, oil, or flammable liquids or combustible materials shall not be used.

(b) *Manufacturer's Instructions.* The garment manufacturer's instructions for care and maintenance of arc-rated apparel shall be followed.

(c) *Storage.* Arc-rated apparel shall be stored in a manner that prevents physical damage; damage from moisture, dust, or other deteriorating agents; or contamination from flammable or combustible materials.

(d) *Cleaning, Repairing, and Affixing Items.* When arc-rated clothing is cleaned, manufacturer's instructions shall be followed. When arc-rated clothing is repaired, the same arc-rated materials used to manufacture the arc-rated clothing shall be used to provide repairs.

Informational Note No. 1: The purpose of following manufacturer's instructions is to avoid the loss of protection and to remove contaminants such as hydrocarbons and metallic and disease-causing contaminants that could compromise safety.

Informational Note No. 2: Additional guidance is provided in ASTM F1506, *Standard Performance Specification for Flame Resistant and Electric Arc Rated Protective Clothing Worn by Workers Exposed to Flames and Electric Arcs*, when trim, name tags, logos, or any combination thereof are affixed to arc-rated clothing.

Informational Note No. 3: Additional guidance is provided in ASTM F1449, *Standard Guide for Industrial Laundering of Flame, Thermal, and Arc Resistant Clothing*, and ASTM F2757, *Standard Guide for Home Laundering Care and Maintenance of Flame, Thermal, and Arc Resistant Clothing*.

Δ **(14) Standards for PPE.**

(a) *General.* PPE shall conform to applicable state, federal, or local codes and standards.

Informational Note No. 1: The standards listed in Table 130.7(C)(14), which is part of this Informational Note, are examples of standards that contain information on the care, inspection, testing, and manufacturing of PPE.

Informational Note No. 2: Non-arc-rated or flammable fabrics are not covered by any of the standards in Table 130.7(C)(14), Informational Note. See 130.7(C)(11) and 130.7(C)(12).

(b) *Conformity Assessment.* All suppliers or manufacturers of PPE shall demonstrate conformity with an appropriate product standard by one of the following methods:

(1) Self-declaration with a Supplier's Declaration of Conformity
(2) Self-declaration under a registered quality management system and product testing by an accredited laboratory and a Supplier's Declaration of Conformity
(3) Certification by an accredited independent third-party certification organization

Informational Note No. 1: Examples of a process for conformity assessment to an appropriate product standard can be found in ANSI/ISEA 125, *American National Standard for Conformity Assessment of Safety and Personal Protective Equipment*. See H.4

Informational Note No. 2: An example of a process to accredit independent third-party certification organizations is ISO 17065, *Conformity assessment — Requirements for bodies certifying products, processes, and services.*

(c) *Marking.* All suppliers or manufacturers of PPE shall provide the following information on the PPE, on the smallest unit container, or contained within the manufacturer's instructions:

(1) Name of manufacturer
(2) Product performance standards to which the product conforms
(3) Arc rating where appropriate for the equipment
(4) One or more identifiers such as model, serial number, lot number, or traceability code
(5) Care instructions

Δ **(15) Arc Flash PPE Category Method.** The requirements of 130.7(C)(15) shall apply when the arc flash PPE category method is used for the selection of arc flash PPE.

(a) *Alternating Current (ac) Equipment.* When the arc flash risk assessment performed in accordance with 130.5 indicates that arc flash PPE is required and the arc flash PPE category method is used for the selection of PPE for ac systems in lieu of the incident energy analysis of 130.5(G), Table 130.7(C)(15)(a) shall be used to determine the arc flash PPE category. The estimated maximum available fault current, maximum fault-clearing times, and minimum working distances for various ac equipment types or classifications are listed in

Table 130.7(C)(15)(a). An incident energy analysis shall be required in accordance with 130.5(G) for the following:

(1) Power systems with greater than the estimated maximum available fault current
(2) Power systems with longer than the maximum fault clearing times
(3) Less than the minimum working distance

(b) *Direct Current (dc) Equipment.* When the arc flash risk assessment performed in accordance with 130.5(G) indicates that arc flash PPE is required and the arc flash PPE category method is used for the selection of PPE for dc systems in lieu of the incident energy analysis of 130.5(G), Table 130.7(C)(15)(b) shall be used to determine the arc flash PPE category. The estimated maximum available fault current, maximum arc duration, and working distances for dc equipment are listed in 130.7(C)(15)(b). An incident energy analysis shall be required in accordance with 130.5(G) for the following:

(1) Power systems with greater than the estimated maximum available fault current
(2) Power systems with longer than the maximum arc duration
(3) Less than the minimum working distance

Informational Note No.1: The arc flash PPE category of the protective clothing and equipment is generally based on determination of the estimated exposure level.

Informational Note No.2: In most cases, closed doors do not provide enough protection to eliminate the need for PPE in situations in which the state of the equipment is known to readily change (e.g., doors open or closed, rack in or rack out).

(c) *Protective Clothing and Personal Protective Equipment (PPE).* Once the arc flash PPE category has been identified from Table 130.7(C)(15)(a) or Table 130.7(C)(15)(b), Table 130.7(C)(15)(c) shall be used to determine the required PPE. Table 130.7(C)(15)(c) lists the requirements for PPE based on arc flash PPE categories 1 through 4. This clothing and equipment shall be used when working within the arc flash boundary. The use of PPE other than or in addition to that listed shall be permitted provided it meets 130.7(C)(7).

Informational Note No. 1: See Informative Annex H for a suggested simplified approach to ensure adequate PPE for electrical workers within facilities with large and diverse electrical systems.

Informational Note No. 2: The PPE requirements of this section are intended to protect a person from arc flash hazards. While some situations could result in burns to the skin even with the protection described in Table 130.7(C)(15)(c), burn injury should be reduced and survivable. Due to the explosive effect of some arc events, physical trauma injuries could occur. The PPE requirements of this section do not address protection against physical trauma other than exposure to the thermal effects of an arc flash.

Informational Note No. 3: The arc rating for a particular clothing system can be obtained from the arc-rated clothing manufacturer.

Δ **Table 130.7(C)(14) Informational Note: Standards for PPE**

Subject	Document Title	Document Number
Clothing — Arc Rated	Standard Performance Specification for Flame Resistant and Electric Arc Rated Protective Clothing Worn by Workers Exposed to Flames and Electric Arc	ASTM F1506
	Standard Guide for Industrial Laundering of Flame, Thermal, and Arc Resistant Clothing	ASTM F1449
	Standard Guide for Home Laundering Care and Maintenance of Flame, Thermal and Arc Resistant Clothing	ASTM F2757
	Live working — Protective clothing against the thermal hazards of an electric arc — Part 1-1: Test methods — Method 1: Determination of the arc rating (ELIM, ATPV, and/or EBT) of clothing materials and of protective clothing using an open arc	IEC 61482–1–1
	Live working — Protective clothing against the thermal hazards of an electric arc — Part 2: Requirements	IEC 61482–2
Aprons — Insulating	Standard Specification for Electrically Insulating Aprons	ASTM F2677
Eye and Face Protection — General	American National Standard for Occupational and Educational Professional Eye and Face Protection	ANSI/ISEA Z87.1
Face — Arc Rated	Standard Test Method for Determining the Arc Rating and Standard Specification for Personal Eye or Face Protective Products	ASTM F2178
Fall Protection	Standard Specification for Personal Climbing Equipment	ASTM F887
Footwear — Dielectric Specification	Standard Specification for Dielectric Footwear	ASTM F1117
Footwear — Dielectric Test Method	Standard Test Method for Determining Dielectric Strength of Dielectric Footwear	ASTM F1116
Footwear — Standard Performance Specification	Standard Specification for Performance Requirements for Protective (Safety) Toe Cap Footwear	ASTM F2413
Footwear — Standard Test Method	Standard Test Methods for Foot Protections	ASTM F2412
Gloves — Arc Rated	Standard Test Method for Determining Arc Ratings of Hand Protective Products Developed and Used for Electrical Arc Flash Protection	ASTM F2675/F2675M
Gloves — Leather Protectors	Standard Specification for Leather Protectors for Rubber Insulating Gloves and Mittens	ASTM F696
Gloves — Rubber Insulating	Standard Specification for Rubber Insulating Gloves	ASTM D120
Gloves and Sleeves — In-Service Care	Standard Specification for In-Service Care of Insulating Gloves and Sleeves	ASTM F496
Head Protection — Hard Hats	American National Standard for Head Protection	ANSI/ISEA Z89.1
Rainwear — Arc Rated	Standard Specification for Arc and Flame Resistant Rainwear	ASTM F1891
Rubber Protective Products — Visual Inspection	Standard Guide for Visual Inspection of Electrical Protective Rubber Products	ASTM F1236
Sleeves — Insulating	Standard Specification for Rubber Insulating Sleeves	ASTM D1051

Shaded text = Revisions.   Δ = Text deletions and figure/table revisions.   • = Section deletions.   *N* = New material.

Δ **Table 130.7(C)(15)(a) Arc Flash PPE Categories for Alternating Current (ac) Systems**

Equipment	Arc Flash PPE Category	Arc Flash Boundary
Panelboards or other equipment rated 240 volts and below Parameters: Maximum of 25 kA available fault current; maximum of 0.03 sec (2 cycles) fault clearing time; minimum working distance 455 mm (18 in.)	1	485 mm (19 in.)
Panelboards or other equipment rated greater than 240 volts and up to 600 volts Parameters: Maximum of 25 kA available fault current; maximum of 0.03 sec (2 cycles) fault clearing time; minimum working distance 455 mm (18 in.)	2	900 mm (3 ft)
600-volt class motor control centers (MCCs) Parameters: Maximum of 65 kA available fault current; maximum of 0.03 sec (2 cycles) fault clearing time; minimum working distance 455 mm (18 in.)	2	1.5 m (5 ft)
600-volt class motor control centers (MCCs) Parameters: Maximum of 42 kA available fault current; maximum of 0.33 sec (20 cycles) fault clearing time; minimum working distance 455 mm (18 in.)	4	4.3 m (14 ft)
600-volt class switchgear (with power circuit breakers or fused switches) and 600-volt class switchboards Parameters: Maximum of 35 kA available fault current; maximum of up to 0.5 sec (30 cycles) fault clearing time; minimum working distance 455 mm (18 in.)	4	6 m (20 ft)
Other 600-volt class (277 volts through 600 volts, nominal) equipment Parameters: Maximum of 65 kA available fault current; maximum of 0.03 sec (2 cycles) fault clearing time; minimum working distance 455 mm (18 in.)	2	1.5 m (5 ft)
NEMA E2 (fused contactor) motor starters, 2.3 kV through 7.2 kV Parameters: Maximum of 35 kA available fault current; maximum of up to 0.24 sec (15 cycles) fault clearing time; minimum working distance 910 mm (36 in.)	4	12 m (40 ft)
Metal-clad switchgear, 1 kV through 15 kV Parameters: Maximum of 35 kA available fault current; maximum of up to 0.24 sec (15 cycles) fault clearing time; minimum working distance 910 mm (36 in.)	4	12 m (40 ft)
Metal enclosed interrupter switchgear, fused or unfused type construction, 1 kV through 15 kV Parameters: Maximum of 35 kA available fault current; maximum of 0.24 sec (15 cycles) fault clearing time; minimum working distance 910 mm (36 in.)	4	12 m (40 ft)
Other equipment 1 kV through 15 kV Parameters: Maximum of 35 kA available fault current; maximum of up to 0.24 sec (15 cycles) fault clearing time; minimum working distance 910 mm (36 in.)	4	12 m (40 ft)
Arc-resistant equipment up to 600-volt class Parameters: DOORS CLOSED and SECURED; with an available fault current and a fault clearing time that does not exceed the arc-resistant rating of the equipment*	N/A	N/A
Arc-resistant equipment 1 kV through 15 kV Parameters: DOORS CLOSED and SECURED; with an available fault current and a fault clearing time that does not exceed the arc-resistant rating of the equipment*	N/A	N/A

N/A: Not applicable

Note:

For equipment rated 600 volts and below and protected by upstream current-limiting fuses or current-limiting molded case circuit breakers sized at 200 amperes or less, the arc flash PPE category can be reduced by one number but not below arc flash PPE category 1.

*For DOORS OPEN refer to the corresponding non-arc-resistant equipment section of this table.

Informational Note No. 1 to Table 130.7(C)(15)(a): The following are typical fault clearing times of overcurrent protective devices:

(1) 0.5 cycle fault clearing time is typical for current-limiting fuses and current-limiting molded case circuit breakers when the fault current is within the current limiting range.

(2) 1.5 cycle fault clearing time is typical for molded case circuit breakers rated less than 1000 volts with an instantaneous integral trip.

(3) 3.0 cycle fault clearing time is typical for insulated case circuit breakers rated less than 1000 volts with an instantaneous integral trip or relay operated trip.

(4) 5.0 cycle fault clearing time is typical for relay operated circuit breakers rated 1 kV to 35 kV when the relay operates in the instantaneous range (i.e., "no intentional delay").

(5) 20 cycle fault clearing time is typical for low-voltage power and insulated case circuit breakers with a short time fault clearing delay for motor inrush.

(6) 30 cycle fault clearing time is typical for low-voltage power and insulated case circuit breakers with a short time fault clearing delay without instantaneous trip.

Informational Note No. 2 to Table 130.7(C)(15)(a): See Table 1 of IEEE 1584, *Guide for Performing Arc Flash Hazard Calculations*, for further information regarding list items (2) through (4) in Informational Note No. 1.

Informational Note No. 3 to Table 130.7(C)(15)(a): An example of a standard that provides information for arc-resistant equipment referred to in Table 130.7(C)(15)(a) is IEEE C37.20.7, *Guide for Testing Switchgear Rated Up to 52 kV for Internal Arcing Faults*.

Informational Note No. 4 to Table 130.7(C)(15)(a): See O.2.4(9) for information on arc-resistant equipment.

Δ **Table 130.7(C)(15)(b) Arc Flash PPE Categories for dc Systems**

Equipment	Arc Flash PPE Category	Arc Flash Boundary
Storage batteries, dc switchboards, and other dc supply sources Parameters: Greater than or equal to 100 volts and less than or equal to 250 volts Maximum arc duration and minimum working distance: 2 sec @ 455 mm (18 in.)		
Available fault current less than 4 kA	2	900 mm (3 ft)
Available fault current greater than or equal to 4 kA and less than 7 kA	2	1.2 m (4 ft)
Available fault current greater than or equal to 7 kA and less than 15 kA	3	1.8 m (6 ft)
Storage batteries, dc switchboards, and other dc supply sources Parameters: Greater than 250 volts and less than or equal to 600 volts Maximum arc duration and minimum working distance: 2 sec @ 455 mm (18 in.)		
Available fault current less than 1.5 kA	2	900 mm (3 ft)
Available fault current greater than or equal to 1.5 kA and less than 3 kA	2	1.2 m (4 ft)
Available fault current greater than or equal to 3 kA and less than 7 kA	3	1.8 m (6 ft.)
Available fault current greater than or equal to 7 kA and less than 10 kA	4	2.5 m (8 ft)

Notes:
(1) Apparel that can be expected to be exposed to electrolyte must meet both of the following conditions:
  (a) Be evaluated for electrolyte protection

  Informational Note: ASTM F1296, *Standard Guide for Evaluating Chemical Protective Clothing*, contains information on evaluating apparel for protection from electrolyte.
  (b) Be arc rated

  Informational Note: ASTM F1891, *Standard Specification for Arc and Flame Resistant Rainwear*, contains information on evaluating arc-rated apparel.
(2) A two-second arc duration is assumed if there is no overcurrent protective device (OCPD) or if the fault clearing time is not known. If the fault clearing time is known and is less than 2 seconds, an incident energy analysis could provide a more representative result.

  Informational Note No. 1: When determining available fault current, the effects of cables and any other impedances in the circuit should be included. Power system modeling is the best method to determine the available short-circuit current at the point of the arc. Battery cell short-circuit current can be obtained from the battery manufacturer. See D.5 for the basis for table values and alternative methods to determine dc incident energy. Methods should be used with good engineering judgment.

  Informational Note No. 2: The methods for estimating the dc arc flash incident energy that were used to determine the categories for this table are based on open-air incident energy calculations. Open-air calculations were used because many battery systems and other dc process systems are in open areas or rooms. If the specific task is within an enclosure, it would be prudent to consider additional PPE protection beyond the value shown in this table.

Δ **Table 130.7(C)(15)(c) Personal Protective Equipment (PPE)**

Arc-Flash PPE Category	PPE
1	**Arc-Rated Clothing, Minimum Arc Rating of 4 cal/cm² (16.75 J/cm²)**[a] Arc-rated long-sleeve shirt and pants or arc-rated coverall Arc-rated face shield[b] or arc flash suit hood Arc-rated jacket, parka, high-visibility apparel, rainwear, or hard hat liner (AN)[f] **Protective Equipment** Hard hat Safety glasses or safety goggles (SR) Hearing protection (ear canal inserts)[c] Heavy-duty leather gloves, arc-rated gloves, or rubber insulating gloves with leather protectors (SR)[d] Leather footwear[e] (AN)
2	**Arc-Rated Clothing, Minimum Arc Rating of 8 cal/cm² (33.5 J/cm²)**[a] Arc-rated long-sleeve shirt and pants or arc-rated coverall Arc-rated flash suit hood or arc-rated face shield[b] and arc-rated balaclava Arc-rated jacket, parka, high-visibility apparel, rainwear, or hard hat liner (AN)[f] **Protective Equipment** Hard hat Safety glasses or safety goggles (SR) Hearing protection (ear canal inserts)[c] Heavy-duty leather gloves, arc-rated gloves, or rubber insulating gloves with leather protectors (SR)[d] Leather footwear[e]
3	**Arc-Rated Clothing Selected so That the System Arc Rating Meets the Required Minimum Arc Rating of 25 cal/cm² (104.7 J/cm²)**[a] Arc-rated long-sleeve shirt (AR) Arc-rated pants (AR) Arc-rated coverall (AR) Arc-rated arc flash suit jacket (AR) Arc-rated arc flash suit pants (AR) Arc-rated arc flash suit hood Arc-rated gloves or rubber insulating gloves with leather protectors (SR)[d] Arc-rated jacket, parka, high-visibility apparel, rainwear, or hard hat liner (AN)[f] **Protective Equipment** Hard hat Safety glasses or safety goggles (SR) Hearing protection (ear canal inserts)[c] Leather footwear[e]
4	**Arc-Rated Clothing Selected so That the System Arc Rating Meets the Required Minimum Arc Rating of 40 cal/cm² (167.5 J/cm²)**[a] Arc-rated long-sleeve shirt (AR) Arc-rated pants (AR) Arc-rated coverall (AR) Arc-rated arc flash suit jacket (AR) Arc-rated arc flash suit pants (AR) Arc-rated arc flash suit hood Arc-rated gloves or rubber insulating gloves with leather protectors (SR)[d] Arc-rated jacket, parka, high-visibility apparel, rainwear, or hard hat liner (AN)[f] **Protective Equipment** Hard hat Safety glasses or safety goggles (SR) Hearing protection (ear canal inserts)[c] Leather footwear[e]

AN: As needed (optional). AR: As required. SR: Selection required.

[a]*Arc rating* is defined in Article 100.

[b]Face shields are to have wrap-around guarding to protect not only the face but also the forehead, ears, and neck, or, alternatively, an arc-rated arc flash suit hood is required to be worn.

[c]Other types of hearing protection are permitted to be used in lieu of or in addition to ear canal inserts provided they are worn under an arc-rated arc flash suit hood.

[d]Rubber insulating gloves with leather protectors provide arc flash protection in addition to shock protection. Higher class rubber insulating gloves with leather protectors, due to their increased material thickness, provide increased arc flash protection.

[e]Footwear other than leather or dielectric shall be permitted to be used provided it has been tested to demonstrate no ignition, melting or dripping at the minimum arc rating for the respective arc flash PPE category.

[f]The arc rating of outer layers worn over arc-rated clothing as protection from the elements or for other safety purposes, and that are not used as part of a layered system, shall not be required to be equal to or greater than the estimated incident energy exposure.

Δ **(D) Other Protective Equipment.**

Δ **(1) Insulated Tools and Equipment.** Tools and handling equipment used within the restricted approach boundary shall be insulated. Insulated tools shall be protected from damage to the insulating material.

Informational Note: See 130.4(E), Shock Protection Boundaries.

(a) *Requirements for Insulated Tools.* The following requirements shall apply to insulated tools:

(1) Insulated tools shall be rated for the voltages on which they are used.

(2) Insulated tools shall be designed and constructed for the environment to which they are exposed and the manner in which they are used.

(3) Insulated tools and equipment shall be inspected prior to each use. The inspection shall look for damage to the insulation or damage that can limit the tool from performing its intended function or could increase the potential for an incident (e.g., damaged tip on a screwdriver).

(b) *Fuse or Fuseholder Handling Equipment.* Fuse or fuseholder handling equipment, insulated for the circuit voltage, shall be used to remove or install a fuse if the fuse terminals are energized.

(c) *Ropes and Handlines.* Ropes and handlines used within the limited approach boundary shall be nonconductive.

(d) *Fiberglass-Reinforced Plastic Rods.* Fiberglass-reinforced plastic rod and tube used for live-line tools shall meet the requirements of applicable portions of electrical codes and standards dealing with electrical installation requirements.

Informational Note: For further information concerning electrical codes and standards dealing with installation requirements, refer to ASTM F711, *Standard Specification for Fiberglass-Reinforced Plastic (FRP) Rod and Tube Used in Live Line Tools.*

(e) *Portable Ladders.* Portable ladders shall have nonconductive side rails when used within the limited approach boundary or where the employee or ladder could contact exposed energized electrical conductors or circuit parts. Nonconductive ladders shall meet the requirements of applicable state, federal, or local codes and standards.

Informational Note: The standards listed in Table 130.7(G), Informational Note are examples of standards that contain information on portable ladders.

N **(2) Barriers.** Exposed energized electrical conductors or circuit parts operating at 50 volts or more shall be guarded by a barrier in accordance with 130.7(D)(2)(a) through 130.7(D)(2)(c) to prevent unintentional contact while an employee is working within the restricted approach boundary of those conductors or circuit parts. Barriers shall be supported to remain in place and shall prevent unintentional contact by a person, tool, or equipment.

(a) *Rubber Insulating Equipment.* Rubber insulating equipment used for protection from unintentional contact with energized conductors or circuit parts shall be rated for the voltage and shall meet the requirements of applicable state, federal, or local codes and standards.

Informational Note: The standards listed in Table 130.7(G), Informational Note are examples of standards that contain information on rubber insulating equipment.

(b) *Voltage-Rated Plastic Guard Equipment.* Plastic guard equipment for protection of employees from unintentional contact with energized conductors or circuit parts, or for protection of employees or energized equipment or material from contact with ground, shall be rated for the voltage and shall meet the requirements of applicable state, federal, or local codes and standards.

Informational Note: The standards listed in Table 130.7(G), Informational Note are examples of standards that contain information on voltage-rated plastic guard equipment.

(c) *Physical or Mechanical Barriers.* Physical or mechanical (field-fabricated) barriers shall be installed no closer than the restricted approach boundary distance given in Table 130.4(E)(a) and Table 130.4(E)(b). While the barrier is being installed, the restricted approach boundary distance specified in Table 130.4(E)(a) and Table 130.4(E)(b) shall be maintained, or the energized conductors or circuit parts shall be placed in an electrically safe work condition.

(E) Alerting Techniques.

(1) Safety Signs and Tags. Safety signs, safety symbols, or tags shall be used where necessary to warn employees about electrical hazards that might endanger them. Such signs and tags shall meet the requirements of applicable state, federal, or local codes and standards.

Informational Note No. 1: Safety signs, tags, and barricades used to identify energized "look-alike" equipment can be employed as an additional preventive measure.

Informational Note No. 2: The standards listed in Table 130.7(G), Informational Note are examples of standards that contain information on safety signs and tags.

(2) Barricades. Barricades shall be used in conjunction with safety signs where it is necessary to prevent or limit employee access to work areas containing energized conductors or circuit parts. Conductive barricades shall not be used where it might increase the likelihood of exposure to an electrical hazard. Barricades shall be placed no closer than the limited approach boundary given in Table 130.4(E)(a) and Table 130.4(E)(b). Where the arc flash boundary is greater than the limited approach boundary, barricades shall not be placed closer than the arc flash boundary.

(3) Attendants. If signs and barricades do not provide sufficient warning and protection from electrical hazards, an attendant shall be stationed to warn and protect employees. The primary duty and responsibility of an attendant providing manual signaling and alerting shall be to keep unqualified employees outside a work area where the unqualified employee might be exposed to electrical hazards. An attendant shall remain in the area as long as there is a potential for employees to be exposed to the electrical hazards.

(F) Look-Alike Equipment. Where work performed on equipment that is de-energized and placed in an electrically safe condition exists in a work area with other energized equipment that is similar in size, shape, and construction, one of the alerting methods in 130.7(E)(1), (2), or (3) shall be employed to prevent the employee from entering look-alike equipment.

(G) Standards for Other Protective Equipment. Other protective equipment required in 130.7(D) shall conform to the applicable state, federal, or local codes and standards.

Informational Note: The standards listed in Table 130.7(G), which is part of this Informational Note, are examples of standards that contain information on other protective equipment.

130.8 Other Precautions for Personnel Activities.

(A) Alertness.

(1) Where Electrical Hazards Might Exist. Employees shall be instructed to be alert at all times where electrical hazards might exist.

△ **(2) When Impaired.** Employees shall not be permitted to work where electrical hazards exist while their alertness is recognizably impaired due to illness, fatigue, or other reasons.

(3) Changes in Scope. Employees shall be instructed to be alert for changes in the job or task that could lead the person outside of the electrically safe work condition or expose the person to additional hazards that were not part of the original plan.

(B) Blind Reaching. Employees shall be instructed not to reach blindly into areas that might contain exposed energized electrical conductors or circuit parts where an electrical hazard exists.

△ **(C) Illumination.**

(1) General. Employees shall not enter spaces where electrical hazards exist unless illumination is provided that enables the employees to perform the work safely.

△ Table 130.7(G) Informational Note: Standards on Other Protective Equipment

Subject	Document	Document Number
Arc Protective Blankets	Standard Test Method for Determining the Protective Performance of an Arc Protective Blanket for Electric Arc Hazards	ASTM F2676
Arc Protective Blankets — Selection, Care, and Use	Standard Guide for Selection, Care, and Use of Arc Protective Blankets	ASTM F3272
Blankets	Standard Specification for Rubber Insulating Blankets	ASTM D1048
Blankets — In-service Care	Standard Specification for In-Service Care of Insulating Blankets	ASTM F479
Covers	Standard Specification for Rubber Insulating Covers	ASTM D1049
Fiberglass Rods — Live Line Tools	Standard Specification for Fiberglass-Reinforced Plastic (FRP) Rod and Tube Used in Live Line Tools	ASTM F711
Insulated Hand Tools	Standard Specification for Insulated and Insulating Hand Tools	ASTM F1505
Ladders	American National Standard for Ladders — Wood — Safety Requirements	ANSI/ ASC A14.1
	American National Standard for Ladders — Fixed — Safety Requirements	ANSI /ASC A14.3
	American National Standard Safety Requirements for Job Made Wooden Ladders	ANSI ASC A14.4
	American National Standard for Ladders — Portable Reinforced Plastic — Safety Requirements	ANSI ASC A14.5
Line Hose	Standard Specification for Rubber Insulating Line Hoses	ASTM D1050
Line Hose and Covers — In-service Care	Standard Specification for In-Service Care of Insulating Line Hose and Covers	ASTM F478
Plastic Guard	Standard Test Methods and Specifications for Electrically Insulating Plastic Guard Equipment for Protection of Workers	ASTM F712
Sheeting	Standard Specification for PVC Insulating Sheeting Standard Specification for Rubber Insulating Sheeting	ASTM F1742 ASTM F2320
Safety Signs and Tags	Series of Standards for Safety Signs and Tags	ANSI Z535
Shield Performance on Live Line Tool	Standard Test Method for Determining the Protective Performance of a Shield Attached on Live Line Tools or on Racking Rods for Electric Arc Hazards	ASTM F2522
Temporary Protective Grounds — In-service Testing	Standard Specification for In-Service Test Methods for Temporary Grounding Jumper Assemblies Used on De-energized Electric Power Lines and Equipment	ASTM F2249
Temporary Protective Grounds — Test Specification	Standard Specification for Temporary Protective Grounds to Be Used on De-energized Electric Power Lines and Equipment	ASTM F855

Δ **(2) Obstructed View of Work Area.** Where lack of illumination or an obstruction precludes observation of the work to be performed, employees shall not perform any task where an electrical hazard exists.

(D) Conductive Articles Being Worn. Conductive articles of jewelry and clothing (such as watchbands, bracelets, rings, key chains, necklaces, metalized aprons, cloth with conductive thread, metal headgear, or metal frame glasses) shall not be worn within the restricted approach boundary or where they present an electrical contact hazard with exposed energized electrical conductors or circuit parts.

(E) Conductive Materials, Tools, and Equipment Being Handled.

(1) General. Conductive materials, tools, and equipment that are in contact with any part of an employee's body shall be handled in a manner that prevents unintentional contact with energized electrical conductors or circuit parts. Such materials and equipment shall include, but are not limited to, long conductive objects, such as ducts, pipes and tubes, conductive hose and rope, metal-lined rules and scales, steel tapes, pulling lines, metal scaffold parts, structural members, bull floats, and chains.

(2) Approach to Energized Electrical Conductors and Circuit Parts. Means shall be employed to ensure that conductive materials approach exposed energized electrical conductors or circuit parts no closer than that permitted by 130.4(F).

Δ **(F) Confined or Enclosed Work Spaces.** When an employee works in a confined or enclosed space (such as a manhole or vault) where an electrical hazard exists, the employer shall provide, and the employee shall use, protective shields, protective barriers, or insulating materials as necessary to protect against electrical hazards.

Δ **(G) Doors and Hinged Panels.** Doors, hinged panels, and the like shall be secured to prevent their swinging into an employee and causing the employee to contact exposed energized electrical conductors or circuit parts where an electrical hazard exists if movement of the door, hinged panel, and the like is likely to create a hazard.

(H) Clear Spaces. Working space required by other codes and standards shall not be used for storage. This space shall be kept clear to permit safe operation and maintenance of electrical equipment.

(I) Housekeeping Duties. Employees shall not perform housekeeping duties inside the limited approach boundary where there is a possibility of contact with energized electrical conductors or circuit parts, unless adequate safeguards (such as insulating equipment or barriers) are provided to prevent contact. Electrically conductive cleaning materials (including conductive solids such as steel wool, metalized cloth, and silicone carbide, as well as conductive liquid solutions) shall not be used inside the limited approach boundary unless procedures to prevent electrical contact are followed.

(J) Occasional Use of Flammable Materials. Where flammable materials are present only occasionally, electric equipment capable of igniting them shall not be permitted to be used, unless measures are taken to prevent hazardous conditions from developing. Such materials shall include, but are not limited to, flammable gases, vapors, or liquids, combustible dust, and ignitible fibers or flyings.

Informational Note: Electrical installation requirements for locations where flammable materials are present on a regular basis are contained in *NFPA 70, National Electrical Code.*

(K) Anticipating Failure. When there is evidence that electric equipment could fail and injure employees, the electric equipment shall be de-energized, unless the employer can demonstrate that de-energizing introduces additional hazards or increased risk or is infeasible because of equipment design or operational limitation. Until the equipment is de-energized or repaired, employees shall be protected from hazards associated with the impending failure of the equipment by suitable barricades and other alerting techniques necessary for safety of the employees.

Informational Note: See 130.7(E) for alerting techniques.

(L) Routine Opening and Closing of Circuits. Load-rated switches, circuit breakers, or other devices specifically designed as disconnecting means shall be used for the opening, reversing, or closing of circuits under load conditions. Cable connectors not of the load-break type, fuses, terminal lugs, and cable splice connections shall not be permitted to be used for such purposes, except in an emergency.

(M) Reclosing Circuits After Protective Device Operation. After a circuit is de-energized by the automatic operation of a circuit protective device, the circuit shall not be manually re-energized until it has been determined that the equipment and circuit can be safely energized. The repetitive manual reclosing of circuit breakers or re-energizing circuits through replaced fuses shall be prohibited. When it is determined from the design of the circuit and the overcurrent devices involved that the automatic operation of a device was caused by an overload rather than a fault condition, examination of the circuit or connected equipment shall not be required before the circuit is re-energized.

(N) Safety Interlocks. Only qualified persons following the requirements for working inside the restricted approach boundary as covered by 130.4(G) shall be permitted to defeat or bypass an electrical safety interlock over which the person has sole control, and then only temporarily while the qualified person is working on the equipment. The safety interlock system shall be returned to its operable condition when the work is completed.

130.9 Work Within the Limited Approach Boundary or Arc Flash Boundary of Overhead Lines.

(A) Uninsulated and Energized. Where work is performed in locations containing uninsulated energized overhead lines that are not guarded or isolated, precautions shall be taken to prevent employees from contacting such lines directly with any unguarded parts of their body or indirectly through conductive materials, tools, or equipment. Where the work to be performed is such that contact with uninsulated energized overhead lines is possible, the lines shall be de-energized and visibly grounded at the point of work or suitably guarded.

(B) Determination of Insulation Rating. A qualified person shall determine if the overhead electrical lines are insulated for the lines' operating voltage.

(C) De-energizing or Guarding. If the lines are to be de-energized, arrangements shall be made with the person or organization that operates or controls the lines to de-energize them and visibly ground them at the point of work. If arrangements are made to use protective measures, such as guarding, isolating, or insulation, these precautions shall prevent each employee from contacting such lines directly with any part of his or her body or indirectly through conductive materials, tools, or equipment.

(D) Employer and Employee Responsibility. The employer and employee shall be responsible for ensuring that guards or protective measures are satisfactory for the conditions. Employees shall comply with established work methods and the use of protective equipment.

(E) Approach Distances for Unqualified Persons. When unqualified persons are working on the ground or in an elevated position near overhead lines, the location shall be such that the employee and the longest conductive object the employee might contact do not come closer to any unguarded, energized overhead power line than the limited approach boundary in Table 130.4(E)(a), column 2 or Table 130.4(E)(b), column 2.

Informational Note: Objects that are not insulated for the voltage involved should be considered to be conductive.

(F) Vehicular and Mechanical Equipment.

(1) Elevated Equipment. Where any vehicle or mechanical equipment structure will be elevated near energized overhead lines, it shall be operated so that the limited approach boundary distance of Table 130.4(E)(a), column 2 or Table 130.4(E)(b), column 2, is maintained. However, under any of the following conditions, the clearances shall be permitted to be reduced:

(1) If the vehicle is in transit with its structure lowered, the limited approach boundary to overhead lines in Table 130.4(E)(a), column 2 or Table 130.4(E)(b), column 2, shall be permitted to be reduced by 1.83 m (6 ft). If insulated barriers, rated for the voltages involved, are installed and they are not part of an attachment to the vehicle, the clearance shall be permitted to be reduced to the design working dimensions of the insulating barrier.

(2) If the equipment is an aerial lift insulated for the voltage involved, and if the work is performed by a qualified person, the clearance (between the uninsulated portion of the aerial lift and the power line) shall be permitted to be reduced to the restricted approach boundary given in Table 130.4(E)(a), column 4 or Table 130.4(E)(b), column 4.

(2) Equipment Contact. Employees standing on the ground shall not contact the vehicle or mechanical equipment or any of its attachments unless either of the following conditions apply:

(1) The employee is using protective equipment rated for the voltage.

(2) The equipment is located so that no uninsulated part of its structure (that portion of the structure that provides a conductive path to employees on the ground) can come closer to the line than permitted in 130.9(F)(1).

(3) Equipment Grounding. If any vehicle or mechanical equipment is capable of having parts of its structure elevated within the limited approach boundary of exposed movable conductors of energized overhead lines and is intentionally grounded, employees working on the ground near the point of grounding shall not stand at the grounding location whenever there is a possibility of overhead line contact. Additional precautions, such as the use of barricades, dielectric overshoe footwear, or insulation, shall be taken to protect employees from hazardous ground potentials (step and touch potential).

Informational Note: Upon contact of the elevated structure with the energized lines, hazardous ground potentials can develop within a few feet or more outward from the grounded point.

130.10 Underground Electrical Lines and Equipment. Before excavation starts where there exists a reasonable possibility of contacting electrical lines or equipment, the employer shall take the necessary steps to contact the appropriate owners or authorities to identify and mark the location of the electrical lines or equipment. When it has been determined that a reasonable possibility of contacting electrical lines or equipment exists, appropriate safe work practices and PPE shall be used during the excavation.

130.11 Cutting or Drilling. Before cutting or drilling into equipment, floors, walls, or structural elements where a likelihood of contacting energized electrical lines or parts exists, the employer shall perform a risk assessment to:

(1) Identify and mark the location of conductors, cables, raceways, or equipment

(2) Create an electrically safe work condition

(3) Identify safe work practices and PPE to be used

Δ **130.12 Cutting, Removing, or Rerouting of Conductors.** Where conductors are de-energized in order to cut, remove, or reroute them and the conductor terminations are not within sight from the point of work, such as where the conductors are remote from the source of supply in a junction or pull box, additional steps to verify absence of voltage or identify the conductors shall be taken prior to cutting, removing, or rerouting the conductors.

Informational Note: Additional steps to be taken where conductors are de-energized in order to cut, remove, or reroute them include, but are not limited to, remotely spiking the conductors, pulling conductors to visually verify movement, remotely cutting the conductors, or other approved methods. Nonshielded conductors could be additionally verified with a noncontact test instrument, and shielded conductors could be verified with devices that identify the conductors.

Chapter 2　Safety-Related Maintenance Requirements

ARTICLE 200
Introduction

△ **200.1 Scope.** Chapter 2 addresses the requirements that follow.

(1) Chapter 2 covers practical safety-related maintenance requirements for electrical equipment and installations in workplaces as included in 90.2. These requirements identify only that maintenance directly associated with employee safety.

(2) Chapter 2 does not prescribe specific maintenance methods or testing procedures. It is left to the employer to choose from the various maintenance methods available to satisfy the requirements of Chapter 2.

(3) For the purpose of Chapter 2, maintenance shall be defined as preserving or restoring the condition of electrical equipment and installations, or parts of either, for the safety of employees who work where exposed to electrical hazards. Repair or replacement of individual portions or parts of equipment shall be permitted without requiring modification or replacement of other portions or parts that are in a safe condition.

> Informational Note: Refer to NFPA 70B, *Recommended Practice for Electrical Equipment Maintenance;* ANSI/NETA MTS, *Standard for Maintenance Testing Specifications for Electrical Power Distribution Equipment and Systems;* and IEEE 3007.2, *Recommended Practice for the Maintenance of Industrial and Commercial Power Systems,* for guidance on maintenance frequency, methods, and tests.

ARTICLE 205
General Maintenance Requirements

205.1 Qualified Persons. Employees who perform maintenance on electrical equipment and installations shall be qualified persons as required in Chapter 1 and shall be trained in, and familiar with, the specific maintenance procedures and tests required.

205.2 Single-Line Diagram. A single-line diagram, where provided for the electrical system, shall be maintained in a legible condition and shall be kept current.

205.3 General Maintenance Requirements. Electrical equipment shall be maintained in accordance with manufacturers' instructions or industry consensus standards to reduce the risk associated with failure. The equipment owner or the owner's designated representative shall be responsible for maintenance of the electrical equipment and documentation.

> Informational Note No. 1: Common industry practice is to apply test or calibration decals to equipment to indicate the test or calibration date and overall condition of equipment that has been tested and maintained in the field. These decals provide the employee immediate indication of last maintenance date

and if the tested device or system was found acceptable on the date of test. This local information can assist the employee in the assessment of overall electrical equipment maintenance status.

> Informational Note No. 2: Noncontact diagnostic methods in addition to scheduled maintenance activities of electrical equipment can assist in the identification of electrical anomalies.

205.4 Overcurrent Protective Devices. Overcurrent protective devices shall be maintained in accordance with the manufacturers' instructions or industry consensus standards. Maintenance, tests, and inspections shall be documented.

205.5 Spaces About Electrical Equipment. All working space and clearances required by electrical codes and standards shall be maintained.

> Informational Note: For further information concerning spaces about electrical equipment, see Article 110, Parts II and III, of *NFPA 70, National Electrical Code.*

205.6 Grounding and Bonding. Equipment, raceway, cable tray, and enclosure bonding and grounding shall be maintained to ensure electrical continuity.

205.7 Guarding of Energized Conductors and Circuit Parts. Enclosures shall be maintained to guard against unintentional contact with exposed energized conductors and circuit parts and other electrical hazards. Covers and doors shall be in place with all associated fasteners and latches secured.

205.8 Safety Equipment. Locks, interlocks, and other safety equipment shall be maintained in proper working condition to accomplish the control purpose.

205.9 Clear Spaces. Access to working space and escape passages shall be kept clear and unobstructed.

205.10 Identification of Components. Identification of components, where required, and safety-related instructions (operating or maintenance), if posted, shall be securely attached and maintained in legible condition.

205.11 Warning Signs. Warning signs, where required, shall be visible, securely attached, and maintained in legible condition.

205.12 Identification of Circuits. Circuit or voltage identification shall be securely affixed and maintained in updated and legible condition.

205.13 Single and Multiple Conductors and Cables. Electrical cables and single and multiple conductors shall be maintained free of damage, shorts, and ground that would expose employees to an electrical hazard.

205.14 Flexible Cords and Cables. Flexible cords and cables shall be maintained to preserve insulation integrity.

(1) Damaged Cords and Cables. Cords and cables shall not have worn, frayed, or damaged areas that would expose employees to an electrical hazard.

(2) Strain Relief. Strain relief of cords and cables shall be maintained to prevent pull from being transmitted directly to joints or terminals.

(3) Repair and Replacement. Cords and cord caps for portable electrical equipment shall be repaired and replaced by qualified personnel and checked for proper polarity, grounding, and continuity prior to returning to service.

205.15 Overhead Line Clearances. For overhead electric lines under the employer's control, grade elevation shall be maintained to preserve no less than the minimum designed vertical and horizontal clearances necessary to minimize risk of unintentional contact.

ARTICLE 210
Substations, Switchgear Assemblies, Switchboards, Panelboards, Motor Control Centers, and Disconnect Switches

210.1 Enclosures. Enclosures shall be kept free of material that would expose employees to an electrical hazard.

210.2 Area Enclosures. Fences, physical protection, enclosures, or other protective means, where required to guard against unauthorized access or unintentional contact with exposed energized conductors and circuit parts, shall be maintained.

210.3 Conductors. Current-carrying conductors (buses, switches, disconnects, joints, and terminations) and bracing shall be maintained to perform as follows:

(1) Conduct rated current without overheating
(2) Withstand available fault current

210.4 Insulation Integrity. Insulation integrity shall be maintained to support the voltage impressed.

210.5 Protective Devices. Protective devices shall be maintained to adequately withstand or interrupt available fault current.

Informational Note: Improper or inadequate maintenance can result in increased opening time of the overcurrent protective device, thus increasing the incident energy.

ARTICLE 215
Premises Wiring

215.1 Covers for Wiring System Components. Covers for wiring system components shall be in place with all associated hardware, and there shall be no unprotected openings.

215.2 Open Wiring Protection. Open wiring protection, such as location or barriers, shall be maintained to prevent unintentional contact.

215.3 Raceways and Cable Trays. Raceways and cable trays shall be maintained to provide physical protection and support for conductors.

ARTICLE 220
Controller Equipment

220.1 Scope. This article shall apply to controllers, including electrical equipment that governs the starting, stopping, direction of motion, acceleration, speed, and protection of rotating equipment and other power utilization apparatus in the workplace.

220.2 Protection and Control Circuitry. Protection and control circuitry used to guard against unintentional contact with exposed energized conductors and circuit parts and to prevent other electrical or mechanical hazards shall be maintained.

ARTICLE 225
Fuses and Circuit Breakers

225.1 Fuses. Fuses shall be maintained free of breaks or cracks in fuse cases, ferrules, and insulators. Fuse clips shall be maintained to provide adequate contact with fuses. Fuseholders for current-limiting fuses shall not be modified to allow the insertion of fuses that are not current-limiting. Non-current limiting fuses shall not be modified to allow their insertion into current-limiting fuseholders.

225.2 Molded-Case Circuit Breakers. Molded-case circuit breakers shall be maintained free of cracks in cases and cracked or broken operating handles.

225.3 Circuit Breaker Testing After Electrical Faults. Circuit breakers that interrupt faults approaching their interrupting ratings shall be inspected and tested in accordance with the manufacturer's instructions.

ARTICLE 230
Rotating Equipment

230.1 Terminal Boxes. Terminal chambers, enclosures, and terminal boxes shall be maintained to guard against unintentional contact with exposed energized conductors and circuit parts and other electrical hazards.

230.2 Guards, Barriers, and Access Plates. Guards, barriers, and access plates shall be maintained to prevent employees from contacting moving or energized parts.

Shaded text = Revisions.   Δ = Text deletions and figure/table revisions.   • = Section deletions.   *N* = New material.

70E–43

ARTICLE 235
Hazardous (Classified) Locations

235.1 Scope. This article covers maintenance requirements in those areas identified as hazardous (classified) locations.

> Informational Note No. 1: These locations need special types of equipment and installation to ensure safe performance under conditions of proper use and maintenance. It is important that inspection authorities and users exercise more than ordinary care with regard to installation and maintenance. The maintenance for specific equipment and materials is covered elsewhere in Chapter 2 and is applicable to hazardous (classified) locations. Other maintenance will ensure that the form of construction and of installation that makes the equipment and materials suitable for the particular location are not compromised.

> Informational Note No. 2: The maintenance needed for specific hazardous (classified) locations depends on the classification of the specific location. The design principles and equipment characteristics, for example, use of positive pressure ventilation, explosionproof, nonincendive, intrinsically safe, and purged and pressurized equipment, that were applied in the installation to meet the requirements of the area classification must also be known. With this information, the employer and the inspection authority are able to determine whether the installation as maintained has retained the condition necessary for a safe workplace.

235.2 Maintenance Requirements for Hazardous (Classified) Locations. Equipment and installations in these locations shall be maintained such that the following criteria are met:

(1) No energized parts are exposed.

Exception to (1): Intrinsically safe and nonincendive circuits.

(2) There are no breaks in conduit systems, fittings, or enclosures from damage, corrosion, or other causes.
(3) All bonding jumpers are securely fastened and intact.
(4) All fittings, boxes, and enclosures with bolted covers have all bolts installed and bolted tight.
(5) All threaded conduit are wrenchtight and enclosure covers are tightened in accordance with the manufacturer's instructions.
(6) There are no open entries into fittings, boxes, or enclosures that would compromise the protection characteristics.
(7) All close-up plugs, breathers, seals, and drains are securely in place.
(8) Marking of luminaires (lighting fixtures) for maximum lamp wattage and temperature rating is legible and not exceeded.
(9) Required markings are secure and legible.

ARTICLE 240
Batteries and Battery Rooms

240.1 Ventilation. When forced or natural ventilation systems are required by the battery system design and are present, they shall be examined and maintained to prevent buildup of explosive mixtures. This maintenance shall include a functional test of any associated detection and alarm systems.

> Informational Note: "Natural ventilation" implies there are no mechanical mechanisms. Maintenance includes activities such as inspection and removal of any obstructions to natural air flow.

240.2 Eye and Body Wash Apparatus. Eye and body wash apparatus shall be maintained in operable condition.

ARTICLE 245
Portable Electric Tools and Equipment

245.1 Maintenance Requirements for Portable Electric Tools and Equipment. Attachment plugs, receptacles, cover plates, and cord connectors shall be maintained such that the following criteria are met:

(1) There are no breaks, damage, or cracks exposing energized conductors and circuit parts.
(2) There are no missing cover plates.
(3) Terminations have no stray strands or loose terminals.
(4) There are no missing, loose, altered, or damaged blades, pins, or contacts.
(5) Polarity is correct.

ARTICLE 250
Personal Safety and Protective Equipment

250.1 Maintenance Requirements for Personal Safety and Protective Equipment. Personal safety and protective equipment such as the following shall be maintained in a safe working condition:

(1) Grounding equipment
(2) Hot sticks
(3) Rubber gloves, sleeves, and leather protectors
(4) Test instruments
(5) Blanket and similar insulating equipment
(6) Insulating mats and similar insulating equipment
(7) Protective barriers
(8) External circuit breaker rack-out devices
(9) Portable lighting units
(10) Temporary protective grounding equipment
(11) Dielectric footwear
(12) Protective clothing
(13) Bypass jumpers
(14) Insulated and insulating hand tools

250.2 Inspection and Testing of Protective Equipment and Protective Tools.

(A) Visual. Safety and protective equipment and protective tools shall be visually inspected for damage and defects before initial use and at intervals thereafter, as service conditions require, but in no case shall the interval exceed 1 year, unless specified otherwise by the applicable state, federal, or local codes and standards.

(B) Testing. The insulation of protective equipment and protective tools, such as items specified in 250.1(1) through 250.1(14), that is used as primary protection from shock hazards and requires an insulation system to ensure protection of personnel, shall be verified by the appropriate test and visual inspection to ascertain that insulating capability has been retained before initial use, and at intervals thereafter, as service conditions and applicable standards and instructions require, but in no case shall the interval exceed 3 years.

250.3 Safety Grounding Equipment.

(A) Inspection. Personal protective ground cable sets shall be inspected for cuts in the protective sheath and damage to the conductors. Clamps and connector strain relief devices shall be checked for tightness. These inspections shall be made at intervals thereafter as service conditions require, but in no case shall the interval exceed 1 year.

(B) Testing. Prior to being returned to service, temporary protective grounding equipment that has been repaired or modified shall be tested. Temporary protective grounding equipment shall be tested as service conditions require.

Informational Note: Guidance for inspecting and testing safety grounds is provided in ASTM F2249, *Standard Specification for In-Service Test Methods for Temporary Grounding Jumper Assemblies Used on De-energized Electric Power Lines and Equipment.*

(C) Grounding and Testing Devices. Grounding and testing devices shall be stored in a clean and dry area. Grounding and testing devices shall be properly inspected and tested before each use.

Informational Note: Guidance for testing of grounding and testing devices is provided in Section 9.5 of IEEE C37.20.6, *Standard for 4.76 kV to 38 kV Rated Ground and Test Devices Used in Enclosures.*

Δ **250.4 Test Instruments.** Test instruments and associated test leads used to verify the absence or presence of voltage shall be maintained to assure functional integrity. The maintenance program shall include functional verification as described in 110.8(E).

Shaded text = Revisions.   Δ = Text deletions and figure/table revisions.   • = Section deletions.   *N* = New material.

70E–45

Chapter 3   Safety Requirements for Special Equipment

ARTICLE 300
Introduction

300.1 Scope. Chapter 3 covers special electrical equipment in the workplace and modifies the general requirements of Chapter 1.

300.2 Responsibility. The employer shall provide safety-related work practices and employee training. The employee shall follow those work practices.

300.3 Organization. Chapter 3 of this standard is divided into articles. Article 300 applies generally. Article 310 applies to electrolytic cells. Article 320 applies to batteries and battery rooms. Article 330 applies to lasers. Article 340 applies to power electronic equipment. Article 350 applies to research and development (R&D) laboratories. Article 360 applies to safety-related requirements for capacitors.

ARTICLE 310
Safety-Related Work Practices for
Electrolytic Cells

310.1 Scope. The requirements of this article shall apply to the electrical safety-related work practices used in the types of electrolytic cell areas.

Informational Note No. 1: See Informative Annex L for a typical application of safeguards in the cell line working zone.

Informational Note No. 2: For further information about electrolytic cells, see *NFPA 70, National Electrical Code*, Article 668.

Informational Note No. 3: For further information about electrical safety-related work practices in electrolytic cell lines, see IEEE 463, *Electrical Safety Practices in Electrolytic Cell Line Working Zones.*

310.2 Definitions. For the purposes of this article, the definitions that follow shall apply.

Battery Effect. A voltage that exists on the cell line after the power supply is disconnected.

Informational Note: Electrolytic cells can exhibit characteristics similar to an electrical storage battery and a shock hazard could exist after the power supply is disconnected from the cell line.

Safeguarding. Safeguards for personnel include the consistent administrative enforcement of safe work practices. Safeguards include training in safe work practices, cell line design, safety equipment, PPE, operating procedures, and work checklists.

310.3 Safety Training.

(A) General. The training requirements of this chapter shall apply to employees exposed to electrical hazards in the cell line working zone defined in 110.6 and shall supplement or modify the requirements of 110.3, 120.5, 130.1, and 130.9.

(B) Training Requirements. Employees shall be trained to understand the specific electrical hazards associated with electrical energy on the cell line. Employees shall be trained in safety-related work practices and procedural requirements to provide protection from the electrical hazards associated with their respective job or task assignment.

310.4 Employee Training.

(A) Qualified Persons.

(1) Training. Qualified persons shall be trained and knowledgeable in the operation of cell line working zone equipment and specific work methods and shall be trained to avoid the electrical hazards that are present. Such persons shall be familiar with the proper use of precautionary techniques and PPE. Training for a qualified person shall include the following:

(1)   Skills and techniques to avoid a shock hazard:

   a. Between exposed energized surfaces, which might include temporarily insulating or guarding parts to permit the employee to work on exposed energized parts

   b. Between exposed energized surfaces and grounded equipment, other grounded objects, or the earth itself, that might include temporarily insulating or guarding parts to permit the employee to work on exposed energized parts

(2)   Method of determining the cell line working zone area boundaries

(2) Qualified Persons. Qualified persons shall be permitted to work within the cell line working zone.

(B) Unqualified Persons.

(1) Training. Unqualified persons shall be trained to identify electrical hazards to which they could be exposed and the proper methods of avoiding the hazards.

(2) In Cell Line Working Zone. When there is a need for an unqualified person to enter the cell line working zone to perform a specific task, that person shall be advised of the electrical hazards by the designated qualified person in charge to ensure that the unqualified person is safeguarded.

310.5 Safeguarding of Employees in the Cell Line Working Zone.

(A) General. Operation and maintenance of electrolytic cell lines might require contact by employees with exposed energized surfaces such as buses, electrolytic cells, and their attachments. The approach distances referred to in Table 130.4(E)(a) and Table 130.4(E)(b) shall not apply to work performed by qualified persons in the cell line working zone. Safeguards such as safety-related work practices and other safeguards shall be used to protect employees from injury while working in the cell line working zone. These safeguards shall be consistent with the nature and extent of the related electrical hazards. Safeguards might be different for energized cell lines and de-energized cell lines. Hazardous battery effect voltages shall be dissipated to consider a cell line de-energized.

Informational Note No. 1: Exposed energized surfaces might not present an electrical hazard. Shock hazards are related to current through the body, producing possible injury or damage to health. Shock severity is a function of many factors, including skin and body resistance, current path through the body, paths in parallel with the body, and system voltage. Arc flash burns and arc blasts are a function of the arcing current and the duration of arc exposure.

Informational Note No. 2: A cell line or group of cell lines operated as a unit for the production of a particular metal, gas, or chemical compound might differ from other cell lines producing the same product because of variations in the particular raw materials used, output capacity, use of proprietary methods or process practices, or other modifying factors. Detailed standard electrical safety-related work practice requirements could become overly restrictive without accomplishing the stated purpose of Chapter 1.

(B) Signs. Permanent signs shall clearly designate electrolytic cell areas.

(C) Arc Flash Risk Assessment. The requirements of 130.5, Arc Flash Risk Assessment, shall not be required for electrolytic cell line working zones.

(1) General. Each task performed in the electrolytic cell line working zone shall be analyzed for the likelihood of arc flash injury. If there is a likelihood of personal injury, appropriate measures shall be taken to protect persons exposed to the arc flash hazards, including one or more of the following:

(1)   Providing appropriate PPE *[see 310.5(D)(2)]* to prevent injury from the arc flash hazard

(2)   Altering work procedures to reduce the likelihood of occurrence of an arc flash incident

(3)   Scheduling the task so that work can be performed when the cell line is de-energized

(2) Routine Tasks. Arc flash risk assessment shall be done for all routine tasks performed in the cell line work zone. The results of the arc flash risk assessment shall be used in training employees in job procedures that minimize the possibility of arc flash hazards. The training shall be included in the requirements of 310.3.

(3) Nonroutine Tasks. Before a nonroutine task is performed in the cell line working zone, an arc flash risk assessment shall be done. If an arc flash hazard is a possibility during nonroutine work, appropriate instructions shall be given to employees involved on how to minimize the risk associated with arc flash.

(4) Arc Flash Hazards. If the likelihood of occurrence of an arc flash hazard exists for either routine or nonroutine tasks, employees shall use appropriate safeguards.

(D) Safeguards. Safeguards shall include one or a combination of the following means.

(1) Insulation. Insulation shall be suitable for the specific conditions, and its components shall be permitted to include glass, porcelain, epoxy coating, rubber, fiberglass, and plastic and, when dry, such materials as concrete, tile, brick, and wood. Insulation shall be permitted to be applied to energized or grounded surfaces.

(2) Personal Protective Equipment (PPE). PPE shall provide protection from electrical hazards. PPE shall include one or more of the following, as determined by authorized management:

(1)   Footwear for wet service
(2)   Gloves for wet service
(3)   Sleeves for wet service
(4)   Footwear for dry service
(5)   Gloves for dry service
(6)   Sleeves for dry service
(7)   Electrically insulated head protection
(8)   Protective clothing
(9)   Eye protection with nonconductive frames
(10) Face shield (polycarbonate or similar nonmelting type)

(a)   *PPE.* Personal and other protective equipment shall be appropriate for conditions, as determined by authorized management.

(b)   *Testing of PPE.* PPE shall be verified with regularity and by methods that are consistent with the exposure of employees to electrical hazards.

(3) Barriers. Barriers shall be devices that prevent contact with energized or grounded surfaces that could present an electrical hazard.

(4) Voltage Equalization. Voltage equalization shall be permitted by bonding a conductive surface to an exposed energized surface, either directly or through a resistance, so that there is insufficient voltage to create an electrical hazard.

(5) Isolation. Isolation shall be established by placing equipment or other items in locations such that employees are unable to simultaneously contact exposed conductive surfaces that could present an electrical hazard.

(6) Safe Work Practices. Employees shall be trained in safe work practices. The training shall include why the work practices in a cell line working zone are different from similar work situations in other areas of the plant. Employees shall comply with established safe work practices and the safe use of protective equipment.

(a)   *Attitude Awareness.* Safe work practice training shall include attitude awareness instruction. Simultaneous contact with energized parts and ground can cause serious electrical shock. Of special importance is the need to be aware of body position where contact may be made with energized parts of the electrolytic cell line and grounded surfaces.

(b)   *Bypassing of Safety Equipment.* Safe work practice training shall include techniques to prevent bypassing the protection of safety equipment. Clothing may bypass protective equipment if the clothing is wet. Trouser legs should be kept at appropriate length, and shirt sleeves should be a good fit so as not to drape while reaching. Jewelry and other metal accessories that may bypass protective equipment shall not be worn while working in the cell line working zone.

(7) Tools. Tools and other devices used in the energized cell line work zone shall be selected to prevent bridging between surfaces at hazardous potential difference.

Informational Note: Tools and other devices of magnetic material could be difficult to handle in the area of energized cells due to their strong dc magnetic fields.

(8) Portable Cutout-Type Switches. Portable cell cutout switches that are connected shall be considered as energized and as an extension of the cell line working zone. Appropriate

---

Shaded text = Revisions.   **Δ** = Text deletions and figure/table revisions.   • = Section deletions.   *N* = New material.

procedures shall be used to ensure proper cutout switch connection and operation.

(9) Cranes and Hoists. Cranes and hoists shall meet the requirements of applicable codes and standards to safeguard employees. Insulation required for safeguarding employees, such as insulated crane hooks, shall be periodically tested.

(10) Attachments. Attachments that extend the cell line electrical hazards beyond the cell line working zone shall use one or more of the following:

(1) Temporary or permanent extension of the cell line working zone
(2) Barriers
(3) Insulating breaks
(4) Isolation

(11) Pacemakers and Metallic Implants. Employees with implanted pacemakers, ferromagnetic medical devices, or other electronic devices vital to life shall not be permitted in cell areas unless written permission is obtained from the employee's physician.

> Informational Note: The American Conference of Governmental Industrial Hygienists (ACGIH) and IEEE 463, *Electrical Safety Practices in Electrolytic Cell Line Working Zones*, recommend that persons with implanted pacemakers should not be exposed to magnetic flux densities above 5 gauss.

(12) Testing. Equipment safeguards for employee protection shall be tested to ensure they are in a safe working condition.

310.6 Portable Tools and Equipment.

> Informational Note: The order of preference for the energy source for portable hand-held equipment is considered to be as follows:
>
> (1) Battery power
> (2) Pneumatic power
> (3) Portable generator
> (4) Nongrounded-type receptacle connected to an ungrounded source

(A) Portable Electrical Equipment. The grounding requirements of 110.9(B) shall not be permitted within an energized cell line working zone. Portable electrical equipment and associated power supplies shall meet the requirements of applicable codes and standards.

(B) Auxiliary Nonelectric Connections. Auxiliary nonelectric connections such as air, water, and gas hoses shall meet the requirements of applicable codes and standards. Pneumatic-powered tools and equipment shall be supplied with nonconductive air hoses in the cell line working zone.

(C) Welding Machines. Welding machine frames shall be considered at cell potential when within the cell line working zone. Safety-related work practices shall require that the cell line not be grounded through the welding machine or its power supply. Welding machines located outside the cell line working zone shall be barricaded to prevent employees from touching the welding machine and ground simultaneously where the welding cables are in the cell line working zone.

(D) Portable Test Equipment. Test equipment in the cell line working zone shall be suitable for use in areas of large magnetic fields and orientation.

> Informational Note: Test equipment that is not suitable for use in such magnetic fields could result in an incorrect response. When such test equipment is removed from the cell line working zone, its performance might return to normal, giving the false impression that the results were correct.

ARTICLE 320
Safety Requirements Related to Batteries and Battery Rooms

320.1 Scope. This article covers electrical safety requirements for the practical safeguarding of employees while working with exposed stationary storage batteries that exceed 50 volts, nominal.

> Informational Note: For additional information on best practices for safely working on stationary batteries, see the following documents:
>
> (1) NFPA 1, *Fire Code*, Chapter 52, Stationary Storage Battery Systems, 2015
> (2) *NFPA 70, National Electrical Code*, Article 480, Storage Batteries, 2014
> (3) IEEE 450, *IEEE Recommended Practice for Maintenance, Testing, and Replacement of Vented Lead-Acid Batteries for Stationary Applications*, 2010
> (4) IEEE 937, *Recommended Practice for Installation and Maintenance of Lead-Acid Batteries for Photovoltaic Systems*, 2007
> (5) IEEE 1106, *IEEE Recommended Practice for Installation, Maintenance, Testing, and Replacement of Vented Nickel-Cadmium Batteries for Stationary Applications*, 2005 (R 2011)
> (6) IEEE 1184, *IEEE Guide for Batteries for Uninterruptible Power Supply Systems*, 2006 (R 2011)
> (7) IEEE 1188, *IEEE Recommended Practice for Maintenance, Testing, and Replacement of Valve-Regulated Lead-Acid (VRLA) Batteries for Stationary Applications*, 1188a-2014
> (8) IEEE 1657, *Recommended Practice for Personnel Qualifications for Installation and Maintenance of Stationary Batteries*, 2009
> (9) OSHA 29 CFR 1910.305(j)(7), "Storage batteries"
> (10) OSHA 29 CFR 1926.441, "Batteries and battery charging"
> (11) DHHS (NIOSH) Publication No. 94-110, *Applications Manual for the Revised NIOSH Lifting Equation*, 1994
> (12) IEEE/ASHRAE 1635, *Guide for the Ventilation and Thermal Management of Batteries for Stationary Applications*, 2012

320.2 Definitions. For the purposes of this article definitions that follow shall apply.

Authorized Personnel. The person in charge of the premises, or other persons appointed or selected by the person in charge of the premises who performs certain duties associated with stationary storage batteries.

Battery. A system consisting of two or more electrochemical cells connected in series or parallel and capable of storing electrical energy received and that can give it back by reconversion.

Shaded text = Revisions. Δ = Text deletions and figure/table revisions. • = Section deletions. *N* = New material.

Battery Room. A room specifically intended for the installation of batteries that have no other protective enclosure.

Cell. The basic electrochemical unit, characterized by an anode and a cathode used to receive, store, and deliver electrical energy.

Electrolyte. A solid, liquid, or aqueous immobilized liquid medium that provides the ion transport mechanism between the positive and negative electrodes of a cell.

Nominal Voltage. The value assigned to a cell or battery of a given voltage class for the purpose of convenient designation; the operating voltage of the cell or system may vary above or below this value.

Pilot Cell. One or more cells chosen to represent the operating parameters of the entire battery (sometimes called "temperature reference" cell).

Prospective Short-Circuit Current. The highest level of fault current that could theoretically occur at a point on a circuit. This is the fault current that can flow in the event of a zero impedance short circuit and if no protection devices operate.

Informational Note: Some batteries have built-in management devices to limit maximum short-circuit current. The determination of the prospective short-circuit current for these batteries assumes that the internal battery management system protection devices are operable.

Valve-Regulated Lead Acid (VRLA) Cell. A lead-acid cell that is sealed with the exception of a valve that opens to the atmosphere when the internal pressure in the cell exceeds atmospheric pressure by a pre-selected amount, and that provides a means for recombination of internally generated oxygen and the suppression of hydrogen gas evolution to limit water consumption.

Vented Cell. A type of cell in which the products of electrolysis and evaporation are allowed to escape freely into the atmosphere as they are generated. (Also called "flooded cell.")

320.3 Safety Procedures.

(A) General Safety Hazards.

(1) Energy Thresholds. Energy exposure levels shall not exceed those identified in the following list unless appropriate controls are implemented:

(1) AC: 50 volts and 5 milliamperes
(2) DC: 100 volts

Informational Note: This information is extracted from the Department of Energy (DOE) Electrical Safety Handbook, DOE-HDBK-1092.

(2) Battery Risk Assessment. Prior to any work on a battery system, a risk assessment shall be performed to identify the chemical, electrical shock, and arc flash hazards and assess the risks associated with the type of tasks to be performed.

Informational Note: For an example of a risk assessment method for work on batteries, see F.7 and Figure F.7 in Informative Annex F.

(3) Battery Room or Enclosure Requirements.

(a) *Personnel Access to Energized Batteries.* Each battery room or battery enclosure shall be accessible only to authorized personnel.

(b) *Illumination.* Employees shall not enter spaces containing batteries unless illumination is provided that enables the employees to perform the work safely.

Informational Note: Battery terminals are normally exposed and pose possible shock hazard. Batteries are also installed in steps or tiers that can cause obstructions.

(4) Apparel. Personnel shall not wear electrically conductive objects such as jewelry while working on a battery system.

(5) Abnormal Battery Conditions. Instrumentation that provides alarms for early warning of abnormal conditions of battery operation, if present, shall be tested annually.

Informational Note: Battery monitoring systems typically include alarms for such conditions as overvoltage, undervoltage, overcurrent, ground fault, and overtemperature. The type of conditions monitored will vary depending upon the battery technology. One source of guidance on monitoring battery systems is IEEE 1491, *Guide for the Selection and Use of Battery Monitoring Equipment in Stationary Applications.*

(6) Warning Signs. The following warning signs or labels shall be posted in appropriate locations:

(1) Electrical hazard warnings indicating the shock hazard due to the battery voltage and the arc flash hazard due to the prospective short-circuit current, and the thermal hazard.

Informational Note No.1: Because internal resistance, prospective short-circuit current, or both are not always provided on battery container labels or data sheets, and because many variables can be introduced into a battery layout, the battery manufacturer should be consulted for accurate data. Variables can include, but are not limited to, the following:

(1) Series connections
(2) Parallel connections
(3) Charging methodology
(4) Temperature
(5) Charge status
(6) Dc distribution cable size and length

Informational Note No. 2: See 130.5(D) for requirements for equipment labeling.

(2) Chemical hazard warnings, applicable to the worst case when multiple battery types are installed in the same space, indicating the following:

a. Potential presence of explosive gas (when applicable to the battery type)
b. Prohibition of open flame and smoking
c. Danger of chemical burns from the electrolyte (when applicable to the battery type)

(3) Notice for personnel to use and wear protective equipment and apparel appropriate to the hazard for the battery

(4) Notice prohibiting access to unauthorized personnel

(B) Electrolyte Hazards.

(1) Battery Activities That Include Handling of Liquid Electrolyte. The following protective equipment shall be available to employees performing any type of service on a battery with liquid electrolyte:

(1) Goggles and face shield appropriate for the electrical hazard and the chemical hazard
(2) Gloves and aprons appropriate for the chemical hazards

(3)   Portable or stationary eye wash facilities and equipment within the work area that are capable of drenching or flushing of the eyes and body for the duration necessary to mitigate injury from the electrolyte hazard.

Informational Note: Guidelines for the use and maintenance of eye wash facilities for vented batteries in nontelecom environments can be found in ANSI/ISEA Z358.1, *American National Standard for Emergency Eye Wash and Shower Equipment.*

(2) Activities That Do Not Include Handling of Electrolyte. Employees performing any activity not involving the handling of electrolyte shall wear safety glasses.

Informational Note: Battery maintenance activities usually do not involve handling electrolyte. Batteries that are hermetically sealed (such as most lithium batteries) or immobilized electrolyte (such as valve-regulated lead acid batteries) present little or no electrolyte hazard. Most modern density meters expose a worker to a quantity of electrolyte too minute to be considered hazardous, if at all. Such work would not be considered handling electrolyte. However, if specific gravity readings are taken using a bulb hydrometer, the risk of exposure is higher — this could be considered to be handling electrolyte, and the requirements of 320.3(B)(1) would apply.

(C) Tools and Equipment.

N **(1) Handles.** Tools and equipment for work on batteries shall be equipped with handles listed as insulated for the maximum working voltage.

N **(2) Contact.** Battery terminals and all electrical conductors shall be kept clear of unintended contact with tools, test equipment, liquid containers, and other foreign objects.

N **(3) Nonsparking Tools.** Nonsparking tools shall be required when the risk assessment required by 110.5(H) justifies their use.

•   **(D) Cell Flame Arresters and Cell Ventilation.** When present, battery cell ventilation openings shall be unobstructed. Cell flame arresters shall be inspected for proper installation and unobstructed ventilation and shall be replaced when necessary in accordance with the manufacturer's instructions.

ARTICLE 330
Safety-Related Work Practices: Lasers

330.1 Scope. This article applies to safety-related work practices for maintaining lasers and their associated equipment.

Informational Note No. 1: For recommendations on laser safety requirements for laser use, see ANSI Z136.1, *Standard for Safe Use of Lasers.*

Informational Note No. 2: For laser product requirements for laser manufacturers, see 21 CFR Part 1040, "Performance Standards for Light-Emitting Products," Sections 1040.10 "Laser products" and 1040.11, "Specific purpose laser products."

330.2 Definitions. For the purposes of this article, the following definitions shall apply.

Field Evaluated. A thorough evaluation of nonlisted or modified equipment in the field that is performed by persons or parties acceptable to the authority having jurisdiction.

Informational Note: The evaluation approval ensures that the equipment meets appropriate codes and standards or is similarly found suitable for a specified purpose.

Laser. A device that produces radiant energy at wavelengths between 180 nm (nanometer) and 1 mm (millimeter) predominantly by controlled stimulated emission. Laser radiation can be highly coherent temporally, spatially, or both.

Laser Energy Source. Any device intended for use in conjunction with a laser to supply energy for the excitation of electrons, ions, or molecules.

Laser Radiation. All electromagnetic radiation emitted by a laser or laser system between 180 nm (nanometers) and 1 mm (millimeters) that is produced as a result of a controlled stimulated emission.

Laser System. A laser in combination with an appropriate laser energy source with or without additional incorporated components.

Protective Barrier. Prevents user access to a hazardous voltage, current, or stored energy area.

330.3 Hazardous Energy.

(A) Voltage and Current. For the purpose of this section, hazardous voltage and current for ac systems is considered greater than or equal to 50 volts ac and 5 mA. For dc systems, hazardous voltage or current is considered greater than or equal to 100 volts dc and 40 mA.

(B) Stored Energy. For the purpose of this article, hazardous stored energy is considered greater than or equal to 0.25 joules at 400 volts or greater, or 1 joule at greater than 100 volts up to 400 volts.

330.4 Electrical Safety Training.

(A) Personnel to Be Trained. Employers shall provide training for all personnel who work on or are near lasers or laser systems with user-accessible hazardous voltage, current, or stored energy (e.g., flashlamp-pumped lasers).

(B) Electrical Safety Training for Work on or with Lasers. Training in electrical safe work practices shall include, but is not limited to, the following:

(1)   Chapter 1 electrical safe work practices
(2)   Electrical hazards associated with laser equipment
(3)   Stored energy hazards, including capacitor bank explosion potential
(4)   Ionizing radiation
(5)   X-ray hazards from high-voltage equipment (>5 kV)
(6)   Assessing the listing status of electrical equipment and the need for field evaluation of nonlisted equipment

330.5 Safeguarding of Persons from Electrical Hazards Associated with Lasers and Laser Systems.

(A) Temporary Guarding. Temporary guarding (e.g., covers, protective insulating barriers) shall be used to limit exposure to any electrical hazard when the permanent laser enclosure covers are removed for maintenance and testing.

(B) Work Requiring an Electrically Safe Work Condition. Work that might expose employees to electrical hazards shall be performed with the equipment in an electrically safe work condition in accordance with 120.1, 120.2, and 110.3.

(C) Energized Electrical Testing. Energized electrical testing, troubleshooting, and voltage testing shall not require an energized work permit in accordance with 130.2(C).

(D) Warning Signs and Labels. Electrical safety warning signs and labels shall be posted as applicable on electrical equipment doors, covers, and protective barriers. The warning signs and labels shall adequately warn of the hazard using effective words, colors, and symbols. These signs and labels shall be permanently affixed to the equipment and shall be of sufficient durability to withstand the environment involved.

(E) Listing. Laser system electrical equipment shall be listed or field evaluated prior to use.

330.6 Responsibility for Electrical Safety. All persons with access to hazardous voltage, current, or stored energy shall be responsible for the following:

(1) Obtaining authorization for work with or on hazardous electrical equipment in lasers and laser systems
(2) Use of Chapter 1 safety-related work practices
(3) Reporting laser equipment failures, accidents, inadequate barriers, and inadequate signage to the employer

ARTICLE 340
Safety-Related Work Practices: Power Electronic Equipment

340.1 Scope. This article shall apply to safety-related work practices around power electronic equipment, including the following:

(1) Electric arc welding equipment
(2) High-power radio, radar, and television transmitting towers and antennas
(3) Industrial dielectric and radio frequency (RF) induction heaters
(4) Shortwave or RF diathermy devices
(5) Process equipment that includes rectifiers and inverters such as the following:

  a. Motor drives
  b. Uninterruptible power supply systems
  c. Lighting controllers

Informational Note: The following standards provide specific guidance for safety-related work practices around power electronic equipment: International Electrotechnical Commission IEC 60479-1, *Effects of Current on Human Beings and Livestock, Part 1: General Aspects*, and the International Commission on Radiological Protection (ICRP) Publication 33, *Protection Against Ionizing Radiation from External Sources Used in Medicine*.

340.2 Definition. For the purposes of this article, the definition that follows shall apply.

Radiation Worker. A person who is required to work in electromagnetic fields, the radiation levels of which exceed those specified for nonoccupational exposure.

340.3 Application. The purpose of this article is to provide guidance for safety personnel in preparing specific safety-related work practices within their industry.

340.4 Hazards Associated with Power Electronic Equipment. The employer and employees shall be aware of the hazards associated with the following:

(1) High voltages within the power supplies
(2) Radio frequency energy–induced high voltages
(3) Effects of RF fields in the vicinity of antennas and antenna transmission lines, which can introduce electrical shock and burns
(4) Ionizing (X-radiation) hazards from magnetrons, klystrons, thyratrons, cathode-ray tubes, and similar devices
(5) Nonionizing RF radiation hazards from the following:

  a. Radar equipment
  b. Radio communication equipment, including broadcast transmitters
  c. Satellite–earth-transmitters
  d. Industrial scientific and medical equipment
  e. RF induction heaters and dielectric heaters
  f. Industrial microwave heaters and diathermy radiators

340.5 Specific Measures for Personnel Safety.

(A) Employer Responsibility. The employer shall be responsible for the following:

(1) Proper training and supervision by properly qualified personnel, including the following:

  a. Identification of associated hazards
  b. Strategies to reduce the risk associated with the hazards
  c. Methods of avoiding or protecting against the hazard
  d. Necessity of reporting any incident that resulted in, or could have resulted in, injury or damage to health
(2) Properly installed equipment
(3) Proper access to the equipment
(4) Availability of the correct tools for operation and maintenance
(5) Proper identification and guarding of dangerous equipment
(6) Provision of complete and accurate circuit diagrams and other published information to the employee prior to the employee starting work (The circuit diagrams should be marked to indicate the components that present an electrical hazard.)
(7) Maintenance of clear and clean work areas around the equipment to be worked on
(8) Provision of adequate and proper illumination of the work area

(B) Employee Responsibility. The employee shall be responsible for the following:

(1) Understanding the hazards associated with the work
(2) Being continuously alert and aware of the possible hazards
(3) Using the proper tools and procedures for the work
(4) Informing the employer of malfunctioning protective measures, such as faulty or inoperable enclosures and locking schemes
(5) Examining all documents provided by the employer relevant to the work to identify the location of components that present an electrical hazard

(6) Maintaining good housekeeping around the equipment and work space

(7) Reporting any incident that resulted in, or could have resulted in, injury or damage to health

(8) Using and appropriately maintaining the PPE and tools required to perform the work safely

ARTICLE 350
Safety-Related Work Requirements:
Research and Development Laboratories

350.1 Scope. The requirements of this article shall apply to the electrical installations in those areas, with custom or special electrical equipment, designated by the facility management for research and development (R&D) or as laboratories.

350.2 Definitions. For the purposes of this article, the definitions that follow shall apply.

Competent Person. A person who meets all the requirements of *qualified person*, as defined in Article 100 in Chapter 1 of this standard and who, in addition, is responsible for all work activities or safety procedures related to custom or special equipment and has detailed knowledge regarding the exposure to electrical hazards, the appropriate control methods to reduce the risk associated with those hazards, and the implementation of those methods.

Field Evaluated. A thorough evaluation of nonlisted or modified equipment in the field that is performed by persons or parties acceptable to the authority having jurisdiction. The evaluation approval ensures that the equipment meets appropriate codes and standards, or is similarly found suitable for a specified purpose.

> Informational Note: For additional information on recommended practices and procedures for the field evaluation of nonlisted equipment, see NFPA 791, *Recommended Practice and Procedures for Unlabeled Electrical Equipment Evaluation*. For help in evaluating whether third-party entities are acceptable to an authority having jurisdiction, see NFPA 790, *Standard for Competency of Third-Party, Field Evaluation Bodies*.

Laboratory. A building, space, room, or group of rooms intended to serve activities involving procedures for investigation, diagnostics, product testing, or use of custom or special electrical components, systems, or equipment.

Research and Development (R&D). An activity in an installation specifically designated for research or development conducted with custom or special electrical equipment.

350.3 Applications of Other Articles. The electrical system for R&D and laboratory applications shall meet the requirements of the remainder of this document, except as amended by Article 350.

> Informational Note: Examples of these applications include low-voltage–high-current power systems; high-voltage–low-current power systems; dc power supplies; capacitors; cable trays for signal cables and other systems, such as steam, water, air, gas, or drainage; and custom-made electronic equipment.

350.4 Electrical Safety Authority (ESA). Each laboratory or R&D system application shall be permitted to assign an ESA to ensure the use of appropriate electrical safety-related work practices and controls. The ESA shall be permitted to be an electrical safety committee, engineer, or equivalent qualified individual. The ESA shall be permitted to delegate authority to an individual or organization within their control.

(A) Responsibility. The ESA shall act in a manner similar to an authority having jurisdiction for R&D electrical systems and electrical safe work practices.

(B) Qualifications. The ESA shall be competent in the following:

(1) The requirements of this standard

(2) Electrical system requirements applicable to the R&D laboratories

350.5 Specific Measures and Controls for Personnel Safety. Each laboratory or R&D system application shall designate a competent person as defined in this article to ensure the use of appropriate electrical safety-related work practices and controls.

(A) Job Briefings. Job briefings shall be performed in accordance with 110.5(I).

Exception: Prior to starting work, a brief discussion shall be permitted if the task and hazards are documented and the employee has reviewed applicable documentation and is qualified for the task.

(B) Personnel Protection. Safety-related work practices shall be used to safeguard employees from injury while they are exposed to electrical hazards from exposed electrical conductors or circuit parts that are or can become energized. The specific safety-related work practices shall be consistent with the electrical hazard(s) and the associated risk. For calibration and adjustment of equipment as it pertains to sensors, motor controllers, control hardware, and other devices that need to be installed inside equipment or control cabinet, surrounded by electrical hazards, the ESA shall define the required PPE based on the risk and exposure.

Use of electrical insulating blankets, covers, or barriers shall be permitted to prevent inadvertent contact to exposed terminals and conductors. Insulated/nonconductive adjustment and alignment tools shall be used where feasible.

350.6 Approval Requirements. The equipment or systems used in the R&D area or in the laboratory shall be listed or field evaluated prior to use.

> Informational Note: Laboratory and R&D equipment or systems can pose unique electrical hazards that might require mitigation. Such hazards include ac and dc, low voltage and high amperage, high voltage and low current, large electromagnetic fields, induced voltages, pulsed power, multiple frequencies, and similar exposures.

350.7 Custom Built, Non-Listed Research Equipment, 1000 Volts or less AC or DC.

(A) Equipment Marking and Documentation.

(1) Marking. Marking of equipment shall be required for, but not limited to, equipment fabricated, designed, or developed for research testing and evaluation of electrical systems. Marking shall sufficiently list all voltages entering and leaving control cabinets, enclosures, and equipment.

Caution, Warning, or Danger labels shall be affixed to the exterior describing specific hazards and safety concerns.

Informational Note: Refer to ANSI Z535, *Series of Standards for Safety Signs and Tags*, for more information on precautionary marking of electrical systems or equipment.

(2) Documentation. Sufficient documentation shall be provided and readily available to personnel that install, operate, and maintain equipment that describes operation, shutdown, safety concerns, and nonstandard installations.

Schematics, drawings, and bill of materials describing power feeds, voltages, currents, and parts used for construction, maintenance, and operation of the equipment shall be provided.

(3) Shutdown Procedures. Safety requirements and emergency shutdown procedures of equipment shall include lockout/tagout (LOTO) requirements. If equipment-specific LOTO is required, then documentation outlining this procedure and PPE requirements shall be made readily available.

(4) Specific Hazards. Specific hazards, other than electrical, associated with research equipment shall be documented and readily available.

(5) Approvals. Drawings, standard operational procedures, and equipment shall be approved by the ESA on site before initial startup. Assembly of equipment shall comply with national standards where applicable unless research application requires exceptions. Equipment that does not meet the applicable standards shall be required to be approved by the ESA. Proper safety shutdown procedures and PPE requirements shall be considered in the absence of grounding and/or bonding.

(B) Tools, Training, and Maintenance. Documentation shall be provided if special tools, unusual PPE, or other equipment is necessary for proper maintenance and operation of equipment. The ESA shall make the determination of appropriate training and qualifications required to perform specific tasks.

350.8 Custom Built, Unlisted Research Equipment, >1000 V AC or DC. Installations shall comply with all requirements of 350.7.

In the event that research equipment requires PPE beyond what is commercially available, the ESA shall determine safe work practices and PPE to be used.

Δ **350.9 Energy Thresholds.** Energy exposure levels shall not exceed those identified in the following list unless appropriate controls are implemented as approved by the ESA:

(1) AC: 50 volts and 5 milliamperes
(2) DC: 100 volts and 40 milliamperes

Informational Note No. 1: This information is extracted from the Department of Energy, *DOE Electrical Safety Handbook*, DOE-HDBK-1092.

Informational Note No. 2: See 360.3 and Informative Annex R for information on capacitor hazards and controls.

350.10 Establishing an Electrically Safe Work Condition. Energized electrical conductors and circuit parts shall be put into an electrically safe work condition before an employee performs work.

Exception: At the discretion of the ESA, alternative methods of ensuring worker safety shall be permitted to be employed for the following conditions:

(1) *Minor tool changes and adjustments, and other normal production operations that are routine, repetitive, or sequential and integral to the use of the equipment for production*
(2) *Minor changes to the unit under test and other minor servicing activities, to include the activities listed under 350.10 Exception condition (1), that take place during research and development*
(3) *Work on cord-and-plug-connected equipment for which exposure to the hazards of unexpected energization or start up is controlled by the following:*

  a. *Unplugging the equipment from the energy source*
  b. *The employee performing the work maintaining exclusive control of the plug*

N

ARTICLE 360
Safety-Related Requirements for Capacitors

N **360.1 Scope.** This article covers the electrical safety-related requirements for the practical safeguarding of employees while working with capacitors that present an electrical hazard.

Informational Note: For more information on working safely with capacitors, see Informative Annex R, Working with Capacitors.

N **360.2 Definitions.**

N **Arc Blast Hazard.** A source of possible injury or damage to health from the energy deposited into acoustical shock-wave and high-velocity shrapnel.

N **Bleed Resistor.** A resistor network connected in parallel with a capacitor's terminals that drains the charge after power has been disconnected.

N **Charge Transfer.** Improper discharging of capacitor networks that results in transferring from one capacitor to another charge instead of fully discharging the stored energy.

N **Dielectric Absorption.** The property of certain capacitors to recharge after being discharged.

Informational Note: A voltage recharge of up to 10 percent can occur a few minutes after the grounding or shorting device has been removed.

N **Discharge Time.** The time required to discharge a capacitor to below a stored energy hazard threshold.

N **Ground Stick.** A device that is used to ensure that the capacitor is discharged by applying it to all terminals of the capacitor element.

Informational Note: This is also called a ground hook and could incorporate power-rated discharge resistors for high-energy applications.

N **Hard Grounding (Low-Z).** The practice of discharging a capacitor through a low impedance, also called Low-Z (impedance) grounding.

N **Hearing Protection Boundary.** Worker distance at which a 1 percent probability of ear damage exists from a 20 kPa (3.0 psi) shock wave.

Shaded text = Revisions.   Δ = Text deletions and figure/table revisions.   • = Section deletions.   *N* = New material.

70E–53

N **Lung Protection Boundary.** Worker distance at which a 1 percent probability of lung damage exists from a 70 kPa (10 psi) shock wave.

N **Soft Grounding (High-Z).** The practice of connecting a capacitor to ground through a power resistor to avoid the hazards related with hard grounding.

N **Time Constant.** The time it takes for voltage to drop by ~63 percent (1/e) during discharge.

N **360.3 Stored Energy Hazard Thresholds.** Appropriate controls shall be applied where any of the following hazard thresholds are exceeded:

(1) Less than 100 volts and greater than 100 joules of stored energy

(2) Greater than or equal to 100 volts and greater than 1.0 joule of stored energy

(3) Greater than or equal to 400 volts and greater than 0.25 joules of stored energy

N **360.4 Specific Measures for Personnel Safety.**

N **(A) Qualification and Training.** The following qualifications and training shall be required for personnel safety:

(1) Employees who perform work on electrical equipment with capacitors that exceed the energy thresholds in 360.3 shall be qualified and shall be trained in, and familiar with, the specific hazards and controls required for safe work.

(2) Unqualified persons who perform work on electrical equipment with capacitors shall be trained in, and familiar with, any electrical safety-related work practices necessary for their safety.

N **(B) Performing a Risk Assessment for Capacitors.** The risk assessment process for capacitors shall follow the overall risk assessment procedures in Chapter 1. If additional protective measures are required, they shall be selected and implemented according to the hierarchy of risk control identified in 110.5(H)(3). When the additional protective measures include the use of PPE, the following shall be determined:

(1) Capacitor voltage and stored energy for the worker exposure. An exposure shall be considered to exist when a conductor or circuit part that could potentially remain energized with hazardous stored energy is exposed.

(2) Thermal hazard. The appropriate thermal PPE shall be selected and used if the stored energy of the exposed part is greater 100 joules.

(3) Shock hazard. The appropriate shock PPE in accordance with 130.7 shall be selected and used if the voltage is greater than or equal to 100 volts.

(4) Arc flash and arc blast hazard at the appropriate working distance. The appropriate protection for the arc flash and arc blast hazard shall be selected, as follows:

(a) Arc flash PPE in accordance with 130.7 shall be selected and used if the incident energy exceeds 1.2 cal/cm^2 (5 J/cm^2) at the working distance.

(b) Hearing protection shall be required where the stored energy exceeds 100 joules.

(c) The lung protection boundary shall be determined if stored energy is above 122 kJ. Employees shall not enter the lung protection boundary.

(d) Alerting techniques in accordance with 130.7(E) shall be used to warn employees of the hazards.

(5) Required test and grounding method. Soft grounding shall be used for stored energy greater than 1000 joules. If capacitors are equipped with bleed resistors, or if using a soft grounding system, the required discharge wait time shall be determined where applicable.

(6) Develop a written procedure that captures all of the required steps to place the equipment in an electrically safe work condition. Include information about the amount of stored energy available, how long to wait after de-energization before opening the enclosure, how to test for absence of voltage, and what to do if there is still stored energy present.

Informational Note No. 1: For more information on calculating capacitor stored energy, arc flash, and arc blast boundaries, see Informative Annex R, Working Safely with Capacitors.

Informational Note No. 2: Heavy duty leather with a minimum thickness of 0.03 in. (0.7 mm) provides protection from thermal hazards.

N **360.5 Establishing an Electrically Safe Work Condition for a Capacitor(s).**

N **(A) Written Procedure.** Where a conductor or circuit part is connected to a capacitor(s) operating at or above the thresholds in 360.3, a written procedure shall be used to document the necessary steps and sequence to discharge the capacitor(s) and place the equipment into an electrically safe work condition. The written procedure shall incorporate the results of the risk assessment performed in 360.5(B) and specify the following at a minimum:

N **(B) Safe Work Practices.** In order to place the capacitor(s) into an electrically safe work condition, a qualified person shall use the appropriate safe work practices and PPE and shall apply the following process for establishing and verifying an electrically safe work condition:

(1) Determine all possible sources of electrical supply to the specific equipment. Check applicable up-to-date drawings, diagrams, and identification tags.

(2) After properly interrupting the load current, open the disconnecting device(s) for each source.

(3) Wherever possible, visually verify that all blades of the disconnecting devices are fully open or that drawout-type circuit breakers are withdrawn to the fully disconnected position.

(4) Apply lockout/tagout devices in accordance with a documented and established policy.

(5) If bleed resistors or automatic discharge systems are applicable, wait the prescribed time for the capacitors to discharge to less than the thresholds in 360.3 and proceed to step (6). For systems without bleed resistors or automatic discharge systems, discharge the capacitors with an adequately rated grounding device (e.g., ground stick). Soft grounding shall be performed above 1000 joules, and remote soft grounding shall be performed above 100 kJ.

(6) Verify that the capacitors are discharged. For capacitors less than 1000 joules, verification shall be permitted to be done either by testing or by grounding. For capacitors between 1000 joules and less than 100 kJ, verification shall be done using testing or soft grounding, then hard grounding. Above 100 kJ, an engineered and redundant system shall be used for remote testing and grounding. An adequately rated portable test instrument shall be used to test between each capacitor terminal and from

each terminal to ground to assure that the capacitor is de-energized.

(7) Before and after each verification, determine that the test instrument is operating satisfactorily through verification on a known dc voltage source. If voltage remains, determine and correct the cause, and repeat step (5) to discharge the capacitors. Where recharging can occur due to dielectric absorption or induced voltages, all the capacitor terminals shall be connected together and grounded with a bare or transparent-insulated wire.

(8) For series capacitors the shorting wires shall be attached across each individual capacitor, and to case.

For single capacitors or for a parallel capacitor bank, the grounding device shall be permitted to be left attached to the capacitor terminals for the duration of the work (e.g., a ground stick).

Exception: Lockout/tagout shall not be required for work on cord- and plug-connected equipment for which exposure to the hazards of unexpected energization of the equipment is controlled by the unplugging of the equipment from the energy source, provided that the plug is under the exclusive control of the employee performing the servicing and maintenance for the duration of the work.

N **360.6 Grounding Sticks.** Grounding sticks shall be provided for qualified persons to safely discharge any residual stored energy contained in capacitors or to hold the capacitor potential at 0 volts. The grounding sticks shall be designed, constructed, installed, and periodically inspected so that the full energy and voltage of the capacitors can be safely discharged.

N **(A) Visual Inspection.** The ground stick shall be visually inspected for defects before each use. All mechanical connections shall be examined for loose connections. Resistors shall be visually inspected for cracks or other defects and electrically tested for proper resistance. The following shall occur if defects or contamination are found:

(1) If any defect or contamination that could adversely affect the insulating qualities or mechanical integrity of the

ground stick is present, the tool shall be removed from service.

(2) If the defect or contamination exists on the grounding stick, then it shall be replaced or repaired and tested before returning to service.

(3) If the defect or contamination exists on the cable, then it shall be replaced or repaired and tested before returning to service.

N **(B) Electrical Testing.** All ground sticks shall be electrically tested as follows:

(1) The ground stick cable shall be tested to verify that the impedance is less than 0.1 ohms to ground every 2 years.

(2) The testing shall be documented.

Exception: The test shall be performed annually if the ground stick is utilized outdoors or in other adverse conditions.

(3) Soft grounding (High-Z) ground sticks with resistors shall be measured and compared to the specified value before each use.

N **(C) Storage and Disposal.** Any residual charge from capacitors shall be removed by discharging before servicing or removal.

(1) All uninstalled capacitors capable of storing 10 joules or greater at their rated voltage shall be short-circuited with a conductor of appropriate size.

(2) When an uninstalled capacitor is discovered without the shorting conductor attached to the terminals, it shall be treated as energized and charged to its full rated voltage until determined safe by a qualified person.

Informational Note: A capacitor that develops an internal open circuit could retain substantial charge internally even though the terminals are short-circuited. Such a capacitor can be hazardous to transport, because the damaged internal wiring could reconnect and discharge the capacitor through the short-circuiting conductor. Any capacitor that shows a significant change in capacitance after a fault could have this problem. Action should be taken to reduce the risk associated with this hazard when it is discovered.

Informative Annex A Informative Publications

A.1 General. The following documents or portions thereof are referenced within this standard for informational purposes only and are thus not part of the requirements of this document.

△ **A.2 NFPA Publications.** National Fire Protection Association, 1 Batterymarch Park, Quincy, MA 02169-7471.

NFPA 70®, *National Electrical Code®*, 2020 edition.

NFPA 1, *Fire Code*, 2018 edition.

NFPA 70B, *Recommended Practice for Electrical Equipment Maintenance*, 2019 edition.

NFPA 790, *Standard for Competency of Third-Party Field Evaluation Bodies*, 2021 edition.

NFPA 791, *Recommended Practice and Procedures for Unlabeled Electrical Equipment Evaluation*, 2021 edition.

A.3 Other Publications.

△ **A.3.1 ANSI Publications.** American National Standards Institute, Inc., 25 West 43rd Street, 4th Floor, New York, NY 10036.

ANSI/ASC A14.1, *American National Standard for Ladders — Wood — Safety Requirements*, 2007.

ANSI/ASC A14.3, *American National Standard for Ladders — Fixed — Safety Requirements*, 2008.

ANSI/ASC A14.4, *American National Standard Safety Requirements for Job Made Wooden Ladders*, 2009.

ANSI/ASC A14.5, *American National Standard for Ladders — Portable Reinforced Plastic — Safety Requirements*, 2007.

ANSI C84.1, *Electric Power Systems and Equipment — Voltage Ratings (60 Hz)*, 2011.

ANSI/AIHA Z10, *American National Standard for Occupational Health and Safety Management Systems*, 2012.

ANSI Z136.1, *Standard for Safe Use of Lasers*, 2014.

ANSI/ASSE Z244.1, *Control of Hazardous Energy — Lockout/Tagout and Alternative Methods*, 2003 (R 2008).

ANSI Z535, *Series of Standards for Safety Signs and Tags*, 2011.

ANSI Z535.4, *Product Safety Signs and Tags Labels*, 2011.

ANSI/NETA MTS, *Standard for Maintenance Testing Specifications for Electrical Power Distribution Equipment and Systems*, 2011.

△ **A.3.2 ASTM Publications.** ASTM International, 100 Barr Harbor Drive, P.O Box C700, West Conshohocken, PA 19428-2959.

ASTM D120, *Standard Specification for Rubber Insulating Gloves*, 2014a.

ASTM D1048, *Standard Specification for Rubber Insulating Blankets*, 2014.

ASTM D1049, *Standard Specification for Rubber Insulating Covers*, 1998 (R 2017).

ASTM D1050, *Standard Specification for Rubber Insulating Line Hoses*, 2005 (R 2017).

ASTM D1051, *Standard Specification for Rubber Insulating Sleeves*, 2014a.

ASTM F478, *Standard Specification for In-Service Care of Insulating Line Hose and Covers*, 2014a.

ASTM F479, *Standard Specification for In-Service Care of Insulating Blankets*, 2006 (R 2017).

ASTM F496, *Standard Specification for In-Service Care of Insulating Gloves and Sleeves*, 2014a.

ASTM F696, *Standard Specification for Leather Protectors for Rubber Insulating Gloves and Mittens*, 2006 (R 2011).

ASTM F711, *Standard Specification for Fiberglass-Reinforced Plastic (FRP) Rod and Tube Used in Live Line Tools*, 2017.

ASTM F712, *Standard Test Methods and Specifications for Electrically Insulating Plastic Guard Equipment for Protection of Workers*, 2006 (R 2011).

ASTM F855, *Standard Specification for Temporary Protective Grounds to Be Used on De-energized Electric Power Lines and Equipment*, 2017.

ASTM F887, *Standard Specification for Personal Climbing Equipment*, 2016.

ASTM F1116, *Standard Test Method for Determining Dielectric Strength of Dielectric Footwear*, 2014a.

ASTM F1117, *Standard Specification for Dielectric Footwear*, 2003 (R 2013).

ASTM F1236, *Standard Guide for Visual Inspection of Electrical Protective Rubber Products*, 2016.

ASTM F1296, *Standard Guide for Evaluating Chemical Protective Clothing*, 2015.

ASTM F1449, *Standard Guide for Industrial Laundering of Flame, Thermal, and Arc Resistant Clothing*, 2015.

ASTM F1505, *Standard Specification for Insulated and Insulating Hand Tools*, 2016.

ASTM F1506, *Standard Performance Specification for Flame Resistant and Electric Arc Rated Protective Clothing Worn by Workers Exposed to Flames and Electric Arcs*, 2018.

ASTM F1742, *Standard Specification for PVC Insulating Sheeting*, 2003 (R 2011).

ASTM F1891, *Standard Specification for Arc and Flame Resistant Rainwear*, 2012.

ASTM F1959/F1959M, *Standard Test Method for Determining the Arc Rating of Materials for Clothing*, 2014.

ASTM F2178, *Standard Test Method for Determining the Arc Rating and Standard Specification for Eye or Face Protective Products*, 2017b.

Shaded text = Revisions.   △ = Text deletions and figure/table revisions.   • = Section deletions.   *N* = New material.

ASTM F2249, *Standard Specification for In-Service Test Methods for Temporary Grounding Jumper Assemblies Used on De-energized Electric Power Lines and Equipment*, 2003 (R 2015).

ASTM F2320, *Standard Specification for Rubber Insulating Sheeting*, 2011.

ASTM F2412, *Standard Test Methods for Foot Protections*, 2018.

ASTM F2413, *Standard Specification for Performance Requirements for Protective (Safety) Toe Cap Footwear*, 2017.

ASTM F2522, *Standard Test Method for Determining the Protective Performance of a Shield Attached on Live Line Tools or on Racking Rods for Electric Arc Hazards*, 2017.

ASTM F2675/F2675M, *Standard Test Method for Determining Arc Ratings of Hand Protective Products Developed and Used for Electrical Arc Flash Protection*, 2013.

ASTM F2676, *Standard Test Method for Determining the Protective Performance of an Arc Protective Blanket for Electric Arc Hazards*, 2016.

ASTM F2677, *Standard Specification for Electrically Insulating Aprons*, (R 2013).

ASTM F2757, *Standard Guide for Home Laundering Care and Maintenance of Flame, Thermal, and Arc Resistant Clothing*, 2016.

ASTM F3272, *Standard Guide for Selection, Care, and Use of Arc Protective Blankets*, 2018.

A.3.3 British Standards Institute, Occupational Health and Safety Assessment Series (OHSAS) Project Group Publications. British Standards Institute, American Headquarters, 12110 Sunset Hills Road, Suite 200, Reston VA 20190-5902.

BS OSHAS 18001, *Occupational Health and Safety Management Systems*, 2007.

△ **A.3.4 CSA Publications.** Canadian Standards Association, 5060 Spectrum Way, Mississauga, ON L4W 5N6, Canada.

CAN/CSA Z1000, *Occupational Health and Safety Management*, 2006 (R 2011).

A.3.5 ICRP Publications. International Commission on Radiological Protection, SE-171 16 Stockholm, Sweden.

ICRP Publication 33, *Protection Against Ionizing Radiation from External Sources Used in Medicine*, March 1982.

△ **A.3.6 IEC Publications.** International Electrotechnical Commission, 3, rue de Varembé, P.O. Box 131, CH-1211 Geneva 20, Switzerland.

IEC TS 60479-1, *Effects of Current on Human Beings and Livestock Part 1: General Aspects*, 2016.

IECTS 60479-2, *Effects of Current on Humans and Livestock, Part 2, Special Aspects*, 2017.

IEC 61243-1, *Live Working — Voltage Detectors — Part 1: Capacitive type to be used for voltages exceeding 1kV a.c.*, 2009.

IEC 61243-2, *Live Working — Voltage Detectors — Part 2: Resistive type to be used for voltages of 1kV to 36 kV a.c.*, 2002.

IEC 61243.3, *Live Working — Voltage Detectors — Part 3: Two-pole low voltage type*, 2014.

△ **A.3.7 IEEE Publications.** Institute of Electrical and Electronics Engineers, IEEE Operations Center, 445 Hoes Lane, P. O. Box 1331, Piscataway, NJ 08855-1331.

IEEE C37.20.7, *Guide for Testing Switchgear Rated up to 52 kV for Internal Arcing Faults*, 2007/Corrigendum 1, 2010.

ANSI/IEEE C2, *National Electrical Safety Code*, 2012, 2017.

IEEE 4, *Standard Techniques for High Voltage Testing*, 2013.

IEEE 450, *IEEE Recommended Practice for Maintenance, Testing, and Replacement of Vented Lead-Acid Batteries for Stationary Applications*, 2010.

IEEE 463, *Electrical Safety Practices in Electrolytic Cell Line Working Zones*, 2013.

IEEE 516, *Guide for Maintenance Methods on Energized Power Lines*, 2009.

IEEE 937, *Recommended Practice for Installation and Maintenance of Lead-Acid Batteries for Photovoltaic Systems*, 2007.

IEEE 946, *Recommended Practice for the Design of DC Auxiliary Power Systems for Generating Systems*, 2004.

IEEE 1106, *Recommended Practice for Installation, Maintenance, Testing, and Replacement of Vented Nickel-Cadmium Batteries for Stationary Applications*, 2010.

IEEE 1184, *Guide for Batteries for Uninterruptible Power Supply Systems*, 2006.

IEEE 1188, *Recommended Practice for Maintenance, Testing, and Replacement of Valve-Regulated Lead-Acid (VRLA) Batteries for Stationary Applications*, 2005 (R 2010).

IEEE 1491, *Guide for Selection and Use of Battery Monitoring Equipment in Stationary Applications*, 2012.

IEEE 1584™, *Guide for Performing Arc Flash Hazard Calculations*, 2018.

IEEE/ASHRAE 1635, *Guide for the Ventilation and Thermal Management of Batteries for Stationary Applications*, 2018.

IEEE 1657, *Recommended Practice for Personnel Qualifications for Installation and Maintenance of Stationary Batteries*, 2009.

IEEE 3007.1, *Recommended Practice for the Operation and Management of Industrial and Commercial Power Systems*, 2010.

IEEE 3007.2, *Recommended Practice for the Maintenance of Industrial and Commercial Power Systems*, 2010.

IEEE 3007.3, *Recommended Practice for Electrical Safety in Industrial and Commercial Power Systems*, 2012.

Ammerman, R. F., Gammon, T., Sen, P. K., and Nelson, J. P., "DC-Arc Models and Incident-Energy Calculations," *IEEE Transactions on Industry Applications*, Vol. 46, No. 5, 2010.

Doan, D. R, "Arc Flash Calculations for Exposures to DC Systems," *IEEE Transactions on Industry Applications*, Vol 46, No. 6, 2010.

Doughty, R. L., T. E. Neal, and H. L. Floyd II, "Predicting Incident Energy to Better Manage the Electric Arc Hazard on 600 V Power Distribution Systems," Record of Conference Papers IEEE IAS 45th Annual Petroleum and Chemical Industry Conference, September 28–30, 1998.

Lee, R., "The Other Electrical Hazard: Electrical Arc Flash Burns," *IEEE Trans. Applications*, Vol. 1A-18, No. 3, May/June 1982.

A.3.8 ISEA Publications. International Safety Equipment Association, 1901 North Moore Street, Arlington, VA 22209-1762.

ANSI/ISEA 125, *American National Standard for Conformity Assessment of Safety and Personal Protective Equipment*, 2014.

ANSI/ISEA Z87.1, *American National Standard for Occupational and Educational Eye and Face Protection*, 2015.

ANSI/ISEA Z89.1, *American National Standard for Head Protection*, 2014.

ANSI/ISEA Z358.1, *American National Standard for Emergency Eye Wash and Shower Equipment*, 2009.

A.3.9 ISO Publications. International Organization for Standardization, 1, Ch. de la Voie-Creuse, Case postale 56, CH-1211 Geneva 20, Switzerland.

ISO 9001, *Quality management systems*, 2015.

ISO 14001, *Environmental Management Systems — Requirements with Guidance for Use*, 2004.

ISO 17025, *General requirements for the competence of testing and calibration laboratories*, 2017.

ISO 17065, *Conformity assessment — Requirements for bodies certifying products, processes and services*, 2012.

ISO 31000, *Risk management*, 2018.

ISO 31010, *Risk management — Risk assessment techniques*,

A.3.10 NIOSH Publications. National Institute for Occupational Safety and Health, Centers for Disease Control and Prevention, 1600 Clifton Road, Atlanta, GA 30333.

DHHS (NIOSH) Publication No. 94-110, *Applications Manual for the Revised NIOSH Lifting Equation*, 1994.

A.3.11 UL Publications. Underwriters Laboratories Inc., 333 Pfingsten Road, Northbrook, IL 60062-2096.

ANSI/UL 943, *Standard for Ground-Fault Circuit Interrupters*, 2006 (R 2012).

UL 943C, *Outline of Investigation for Special Purpose Ground-Fault Circuit-Interrupters*, 2012.

UL 1436, *Outlet Circuit Testers and Other Similar Indicating Devices*, 2016.

UL 61010-1, *Safety Requirements for Electrical Equipment for Measurement, Control, and Laboratory Use, Part 1: General Requirements*, 2012.

UL 61010-2-033, *Safety Requirements for Electrical Equipment for Measurement, Control, and Laboratory Use — Part 2-033: Particular Requirements for Hand-Held Multimeters and Other Meters, for Domestic and Professional use, Capable of Measuring Mains Voltage*, 2014.

△ **A.3.12 Government Publications.** U.S. Government Publishing Office, 732 North Capitol Street, NW, Washington, DC 20401-0001.

Department of Energy, *DOE Electrical Safety Handbook*, DOE-HDBK-1092-2013.

Title 21, Code of Federal Regulations, Part 1040, "Performance Standards for Light-Emitting Products," Sections 1040.10, "Laser products" and 1040.11, "Specific purpose laser products."

Title 29, Code of Federal Regulations, Part 1910, "Occupational Safety and Health Standards," Subpart S, "Electrical."

Title 29, Code of Federal Regulations, Part 1910.137, "Personal Protective Equipment."

Title 29, Code of Federal Regulations, Part 1910.305(j)(7), "Storage Batteries."

Title 29, Code of Federal Regulations, Part 1926, "Safety and Health Regulations for Construction", Subpart K, "Electrical."

Title 29, Code of Federal Regulations, Part 1926.441, "Batteries and Battery Charging."

A.3.13 Other Publications. Charles R. Hummer, Richard J. Pearson, and Donald H. Porschet, *"Safe Distances From a High-Energy Capacitor Bank for Ear and Lung Protection,"* Army Research Laboratory Report, ANL-TN-608, July 2014.

"DC Arc Hazard Assessment Phase II," Copyright Material, Kinectrics Inc., Report No. K-012623-RA-0002-R00.

Occupational Injuries From Electrical Shock and Arc Flash Events Final Report, Richard Campbell and David Dini, Fire Protection Research Foundation, Quincy, MA.

Occupational Electrical Injuries in the US, 2003–2009, James Cawley and Brett C. Banner, ESFI.

Rasmussen, J., "Skills, rules, and knowledge; signals, signs, and symbols, and other distinctions in human performance models," *IEEE Transactions on Systems, Man, and Cybernetics*, (3), 257–266, 1983.

Reason, J., *Human Error*. Cambridge, UK: Cambridge University Press, 1990.

Technical paper ESW 2012-24 presented at IEEE ESW conference, *Arc Flash Hazards, Incident Energy, PPE Ratings and Thermal Burn Injury — A Deeper Look*, Tammy Gammon, Wei-Jen Lee, and Ben Johnson.

Technical Paper ESW 2015-17 presented at IEEE ESW conference, OSHA Subpart V, *Electric Power and Distribution*, April 11, 2014.

Shaded text = Revisions.   △ = Text deletions and figure/table revisions.   • = Section deletions.   *N* = New material.

Informative Annex B Reserved

Informative Annex C   Limits of Approach

This informative annex is not a part of the requirements of this NFPA document but is included for informational purposes only.

C.1 Preparation for Approach. Observing a safe approach distance from exposed energized electrical conductors or circuit parts is an effective means of maintaining electrical safety. As the distance between a person and the exposed energized conductors or circuit parts decreases, the potential for electrical incident increases.

C.1.1 Unqualified Persons, Safe Approach Distance. Unqualified persons are safe when they maintain a distance from the exposed energized conductors or circuit parts, including the longest conductive object being handled, so that they cannot contact or enter a specified air insulation distance to the exposed energized electrical conductors or circuit parts. This safe approach distance is the limited approach boundary. Further, persons must not cross the arc flash boundary unless they are wearing appropriate personal protective clothing and are under the close supervision of a qualified person. Only when continuously escorted by a qualified person should an unqualified person cross the limited approach boundary. Under no circumstance should an unqualified person cross the restricted approach boundary, where special shock protection techniques and equipment are required.

C.1.2 Qualified Persons, Safe Approach Distance.

C.1.2.1 Determine the arc flash boundary and, if the boundary is to be crossed, appropriate arc-rated protective equipment must be utilized.

C.1.2.2 For a person to cross the limited approach boundary and enter the limited space, a person should meet the following criteria:

(1) Be qualified to perform the job/task
(2) Be able to identify the hazards and associated risks with the tasks to be performed

C.1.2.3 To cross the restricted approach boundary and enter the restricted space, qualified persons should meet the following criteria:

(1) As applicable, have an energized electrical work permit authorized by management.
(2) Use personal protective equipment (PPE) that is rated for the voltage and energy level involved.
(3) Minimize the likelihood of bodily contact with exposed energized conductors and circuit parts from inadvertent movement by keeping as much of the body out of the restricted space as possible and using only protected body parts in the space as necessary to accomplish the work.
(4) Use insulated tools and equipment.

(See Figure C.1.2.3.)

C.2 Basis for Distance Values in Tables 130.4(E)(a) and 130.4(E)(b).

C.2.1 General Statement. Columns 2 through 5 of Table 130.4(E)(a) and Table 130.4(E)(b) show various distances from the exposed energized electrical conductors or circuit parts. They include dimensions that are added to a basic minimum air insulation distance. Those basic minimum air insula-

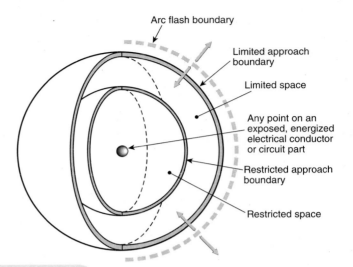

FIGURE C.1.2.3   Limits of Approach.

tion distances for voltages 72.5 kV and under are based on IEEE 4, *Standard Techniques for High Voltage Testing,* Appendix 2B; and voltages over 72.5 kV are based on IEEE 516, *Guide for Maintenance Methods on Energized Power Lines.* The minimum air insulation distances that are required to avoid flashover are as follows:

(1) ≤300 V: 1 mm (0 ft 0.03 in.)
(2) >300 V to ≤750 V: 2 mm (0 ft 0.07 in.)
(3) >750 V to ≤2 kV: 5 mm (0 ft 0.19 in.)
(4) >2 kV to ≤15 kV: 39 mm (0 ft 1.5 in.)
(5) >15 kV to ≤36 kV: 161 mm (0 ft 6.3 in.)
(6) >36 kV to ≤48.3 kV: 254 mm (0 ft 10.0 in.)
(7) >48.3 kV to ≤72.5 kV: 381 mm (1 ft 3.0 in.)
(8) >72.5 kV to ≤121 kV: 640 mm (2 ft 1.2 in.)
(9) >138 kV to ≤145 kV: 778 mm (2 ft 6.6 in.)
(10) >161 kV to ≤169 kV: 915 mm (3 ft 0.0 in.)
(11) >230 kV to ≤242 kV: 1.281 m (4 ft 2.4 in.)
(12) >345 kV to ≤362 kV: 2.282 m (7 ft 5.8 in.)
(13) >500 kV to ≤550 kV: 3.112 m (10 ft 2.5 in.)
(14) >765 kV to ≤800 kV: 4.225 m (13 ft 10.3 in.)

C.2.1.1 Column 1. The voltage ranges have been selected to group voltages that require similar approach distances based on the sum of the electrical withstand distance and an inadvertent movement factor. The value of the upper limit for a range is the maximum voltage for the highest nominal voltage in the range, based on ANSI C84.1, *Electric Power Systems and Equipment — Voltage Ratings (60 Hz).* For single-phase systems, select the range that is equal to the system's maximum phase-to-ground voltage multiplied by 1.732.

C.2.1.2 Column 2. The distances in column 2 are based on OSHA's rule for unqualified persons to maintain a 3.05 m (10 ft) clearance for all voltages up to 50 kV (voltage-to-ground), plus 100 mm (4.0 in.) for each 10 kV over 50 kV.

C.2.1.3 Column 3. The distances in column 3 are based on the following:

(1) ≤750 V: Use *NEC* Table 110.26(A)(1), Working Spaces, Condition 2, for the 151 V to 600 V range.
(2) >750 V to ≤145 kV: Use *NEC* Table 110.34(A), Working Space, Condition 2.
(3) >145 kV: Use OSHA's 3.05 m (10 ft) rules as used in Column 2.

C.2.1.4 Column 4. The distances in column 4 are based on adding to the flashover dimensions shown in C.2.1 the following inadvertent movement distance:

≤300 V: Avoid contact.

Based on experience and precautions for household 120/240-V systems:

>300 V to ≤750 V: Add 304.8 mm (1 ft 0 in.) for inadvertent movement.

These values have been found to be adequate over years of use in ANSI/IEEE C2, *National Electrical Safety Code,* in the approach distances for communication workers.

>72.5 kV: Add 304.8 mm (1 ft 0 in.) for inadvertent movement.

These values have been found to be adequate over years of use in ANSI/IEEE C2, *National Electrical Safety Code,* in the approach distances for supply workers.

Informative Annex D   Incident Energy and Arc Flash Boundary Calculation Methods

This informative annex is not a part of the requirements of this NFPA document but is included for informational purposes only.

D.1 Introduction. Informative Annex D summarizes calculation methods available for calculating arc flash boundary and incident energy. It is important to investigate the limitations of any methods to be used. The limitations of methods summarized in Informative Annex D are described in Table D.1.

D.2 Ralph Lee Calculation Method.

△ D.2.1 Basic Equations for Calculating Arc Flash Boundary Distances. The short-circuit symmetrical ampacity, I_{sc}, from a bolted three-phase fault at the transformer terminals is calculated with the following formula:

$$I_{sc} = \left\{ \left[MVA \text{ Base} \times 10^6 \right] \div \left[1.732 \times V \right] \right\} \times \left\{ 100 \div \%Z \right\} \qquad \textbf{[D.2.1a]}$$

where I_{sc} is in amperes, V is in volts, and $\%Z$ is based on the transformer MVA.

A typical value for the maximum power, P (in MW) in a three-phase arc can be calculated using the following formula:

$$P = \left[\text{maximum bolted fault, in } MVA_{bf} \right] \times 0.707^2 \qquad \textbf{[D.2.1b]}$$

$$P = 1.732 \times V \times I_{sc} \times 10^{-6} \times 0.707^2 \qquad \textbf{[D.2.1c]}$$

The arc flash boundary distance is calculated in accordance with the following formulae:

N

$$D_c = \left[2.65 \times MVA_{bf} \times t \right]^{\frac{1}{2}} \qquad \textbf{[D.2.1d]}$$

$$D_c = \left[53 \times MVA \times t \right]^{\frac{1}{2}} \qquad \textbf{[D.2.1e]}$$

where:
  D_c = distance in feet of person from arc source for a just curable burn (that is, skin temperature remains less than 80°C).
  MVA_{bf} = bolted fault MVA at point involved.
  MVA = MVA rating of transformer. For transformers with MVA ratings below 0.75 MVA, multiply the transformer MVA rating by 1.25.
  t = time of arc exposure in seconds.

The clearing time for a current-limiting fuse is approximately ¼ cycle or 0.004 second if the arcing fault current is in the fuse's current-limiting range. The clearing time of a 5-kV and 15-kV circuit breaker is approximately 0.1 second or 6 cycles if the instantaneous function is installed and operating. This can be broken down as follows: actual breaker time (approximately 2 cycles), plus relay operating time of approximately 1.74 cycles, plus an additional safety margin of 2 cycles, giving a total time of approximately 6 cycles. Additional time must be added if a time delay function is installed and operating.

The formulas used in this explanation are from Ralph Lee, "The Other Electrical Hazard: Electrical Arc Flash Burns," in *IEEE Trans. Industrial Applications.* The calculations are based on the worst-case arc impedance. *(See Table D.2.1.)*

D.2.2 Single-Line Diagram of a Typical Petrochemical Complex. The single-line diagram *(see Figure D.2.2)* illustrates the complexity of a distribution system in a typical petrochemical plant.

△ Table D.1 Limitation of Calculation Methods

Section	Source	Limitations/Parameters
D.2	Lee, "The Other Electrical Hazard: Electrical Arc Flash Burns"	Calculates incident energy and arc flash boundary for arc in open air; conservative over 600 volts and becomes more conservative as voltage increases
D.3	Doughty, et al., "Predicting Incident Energy to Better Manage the Electrical Arc Hazard on 600 V Power Distribution Systems"	Calculates incident energy for three-phase arc on systems rated 600 volts and below; applies to short-circuit currents between 16 kA and 50 kA
D.4	IEEE 1584, *Guide for Performing Arc Flash Hazard Calculations*	Calculates incident energy and arc flash boundary for 208 volts to 15 kV; three-phase; 50 Hz to 60 Hz; 500 amperes to 106,000 amperes short-circuit current (208 volts to 600 volts); 200 amperes to 65,000 amperes short-circuit current (600 volts to 15,000 volts); and conductor gaps of 6.35 mm to 76.2 mm (0.25 in. to 3 in.) for 208 volts to 600 volts and 13 mm to 152 mm (0.75 in. to 10 in.) for 601 volts to 15,000 volts
D.5	Doan, "Arc Flash Calculations for Exposure to DC Systems"	Calculates incident energy for dc systems rated up to 1000 volts dc

Shaded text = Revisions.   **△** = Text deletions and figure/table revisions.   • = Section deletions.   *N* = New material.

Table D.2.1 Flash Burn Hazard at Various Levels in a Large Petrochemical Plant

	(1)	(2)	(3)	(4)	(5)	(6)	(7)	
Bus Nominal Voltage Levels		System (MVA)	Transformer (MVA)	System or Transformer (% Z)	Short-Circuit Symmetrical (A)	Clearing Time of Fault (cycles)	Arc Flash Boundary Typical Distance*	
							SI	U.S.
230 kV		9000		1.11	23,000	6.0	15 m	49.2 ft
13.8 kV		750		9.4	31,300	6.0	1.16 m	3.8 ft
Load side of all 13.8-V fuses		750		9.4	31,300	1.0	184 mm	0.61 ft
4.16 kV			10.0	5.5	25,000	6.0	2.96 m	9.7 ft
4.16 kV			5.0	5.5	12,600	6.0	1.4 m	4.6 ft
Line side of incoming 600-V fuse			2.5	5.5	44,000	60.0–120.0	7 m–11 m	23 ft–36 ft
600-V bus			2.5	5.5	44,000	0.25	268 mm	0.9 ft
600-V bus			1.5	5.5	26,000	6.0	1.6 m	5.4 ft
600-V bus			1.0	5.57	17,000	6.0	1.2 m	4 ft

*Distance from an open arc to limit skin damage to a curable second degree skin burn [less than 80°C (176°F) on skin] in free air.

△ **D.2.3 Sample Calculation.** Many of the electrical characteristics of the systems and equipment are provided in Table D.2.1. The sample calculation is made on the 4160-volt bus 4A or 4B. Table D.2.1 tabulates the results of calculating the arc flash boundary for each part of the system. For this calculation, based on Table D.2.1, the following results are obtained:

(1) Calculation is made on a 4160-volt bus.
(2) Transformer MVA (and base MVA) = 10 MVA.
(3) Transformer impedance on 10 MVA base = 5.5 percent.
(4) Circuit breaker clearing time = 6 cycles.

Using Equation D.2.1(a), calculate the short-circuit current:

N **[D.2.3a]**

$$I_{sc} = \left\{ \left[MVA \text{ Base } \times 10^6 \right] \div \left[1.732 \times V \right] \right\} \times \left\{ 100 \div \%Z \right\}$$
$$= \left\{ \left[10 \times 10^6 \right] \div \left[1.732 \times 4160 \right] \right\} \times \left\{ 100 \div 5.5 \right\}$$
$$= 25,000 \text{ amperes}$$

Using Equation D.2.1(b), calculate the power in the arc:

N **[D.2.3b]**

$$P = 1.732 \times 4160 \times 25,000 \times 10^{-6} \times 0.707^2$$
$$= 91 \text{ MW}$$

Using Equation D.2.1(d), calculate the second degree burn distance:

N **[D.2.3c]**

$$D_c = \left\{ 2.65 \times \left[1.732 \times 25,000 \times 4160 \times 10^{-6} \right] \times 0.1 \right\}^{\frac{1}{2}}$$
$$= 6.9 \text{ or } 7.00 \text{ ft}$$

Or, using Equation D.2.1(e), calculate the second degree burn distance using an alternative method:

N **[D.2.3d]**

$$D_c = \left[53 \times 10 \times 0.1 \right]^{\frac{1}{2}}$$
$$= 7.28 \text{ ft}$$

△ **D.2.4 Calculation of Incident Energy Exposure Greater Than 600 V for an Arc Flash Hazard Analysis.** The equation that follows can be used to predict the incident energy produced by a three-phase arc in open air on systems rated above 600 V. The parameters required to make the calculations follow.

(1) The maximum bolted fault, three-phase short-circuit current available at the equipment.
(2) The total protective device clearing time (upstream of the prospective arc location) at the maximum short-circuit current. If the total protective device clearing time is longer than 2 seconds, consider how long a person is likely to remain in the location of the arc flash. It is likely that a person exposed to an arc flash will move away quickly if it is physically possible, and 2 seconds is a reasonable maximum time for calculations. A person in a bucket truck or a person who has crawled into equipment will need more time to move away. Sound engineering judgment must be used in applying the 2-second maximum clearing time, since there could be circumstances where an employee's egress is inhibited.
(3) The distance from the arc source.
(4) Rated phase-to-phase voltage of the system.

[D.2.4]

$$E = \frac{793 \times F \times V \times t_A}{D^2}$$

where:
E = incident energy, cal/cm^2
F = bolted fault short-circuit current, kA
V = system phase-to-phase voltage, kV
t_A = arc duration, sec
D = distance from the arc source, in.

D.3 Doughty Neal Paper.

D.3.1 Calculation of Incident Energy Exposure. The following equations can be used to predict the incident energy produced by a three-phase arc on systems rated 600 V and below. The results of these equations might not represent the worst case in all situations. It is essential that the equations be used only within the limitations indicated in the definitions of the variables shown under the equations. The equations must be used only under qualified engineering supervision.

> Informational Note: Experimental testing continues to be performed to validate existing incident energy calculations and to determine new formulas.

The parameters required to make the calculations follow.

(1) The maximum bolted fault, three-phase short-circuit current available at the equipment and the minimum fault level at which the arc will self-sustain. (Calculations should be made using the maximum value, and then at lowest fault level at which the arc is self-sustaining. For 480-volt systems, the industry accepted minimum level for a sustaining arcing fault is 38 percent of the available bolted fault, three-phase short-circuit current. The highest incident energy exposure could occur at these lower levels where the overcurrent device could take seconds or minutes to open.)

(2) The total protective device clearing time (upstream of the prospective arc location) at the maximum short-circuit current, and at the minimum fault level at which the arc will sustain itself.

(3) The distance of the worker from the prospective arc for the task to be performed.

Typical working distances used for incident energy calculations are as follows:

(1) Low voltage (600 V and below) MCC and panelboards — 455 mm (18 in.)

(2) Low voltage (600 V and below) switchgear — 610 mm (24 in.)

(3) Medium voltage (above 600 V) switchgear — 910 mm (36 in.)

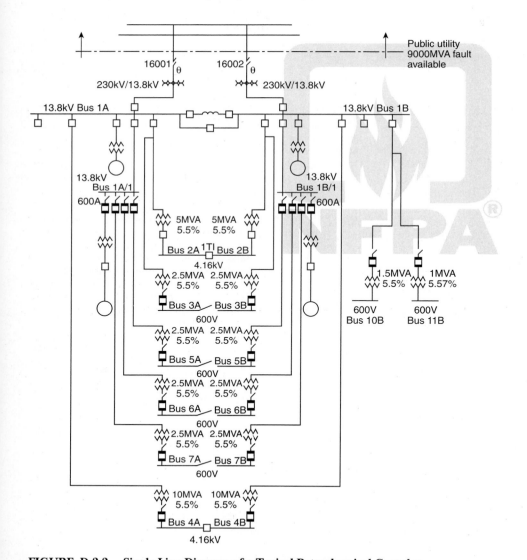

FIGURE D.2.2   Single-Line Diagram of a Typical Petrochemical Complex.

D.3.2 Arc in Open Air. The estimated incident energy for an arc in open air is as follows:

[D.3.2a]

$$E_{MA} = 5271 D_A^{-1.9593} t_A \begin{bmatrix} 0.0016F^2 \\ -0.0076F \\ +0.8938 \end{bmatrix}$$

where:

E_{MA} = maximum open arc incident energy, cal/cm²

D_A = distance from arc electrodes, in. (for distances 18 in. and greater)

t_A = arc duration, sec

F = short-circuit current, kA (for the range of 16 kA to 50 kA)

Sample Calculation: Using Equation D.3.2(a), calculate the maximum open arc incident energy, cal/cm², where D_A = 18 in., t_A = 0.2 second, and F = 20 kA.

[D.3.2b]

$$E_{MA} = 5271 \, D_A^{-1.9593} t_A \begin{bmatrix} 0.0016F^2 - 0.0076F \\ +0.8938 \end{bmatrix}$$

$$= 5271 \times .0035 \times 0.2 [0.0016 \times 400 - 0.0076 \times 20 + 0.8938]$$

$$= 3.69 \times [1.381]$$

$$= 21.33 \, \text{J/cm}^2 \left(5.098 \, \text{cal/cm}^2\right)$$

D.3.3 Arc in a Cubic Box. The estimated incident energy for an arc in a cubic box (20 in. on each side, open on one end) is given in the equation that follows. This equation is applicable to arc flashes emanating from within switchgear, motor control centers, or other electrical equipment enclosures.

[D.3.3a]

$$E_{MB} = 1038.7 D_B^{-1.4738} t_A \begin{bmatrix} 0.0093F^2 \\ -0.3453F \\ +5.9675 \end{bmatrix}$$

where:

E_{MB} = maximum 20 in. cubic box incident energy, cal/cm²

D_B = distance from arc electrodes, in. (for distances 18 in. and greater)

t_A = arc duration, sec

F = short-circuit current, kA (for the range of 16 kA to 50 kA)

Sample Calculation: Using Equation D.3.3(a), calculate the maximum 20 in. cubic box incident energy, cal/cm², using the following:

(1) D_B = 18 in.
(2) t_A = 0.2 sec
(3) F = 20 kA

[D.3.3b]

$$E_{MB} = 1038.7 D_B^{-1.4738} t_A \begin{bmatrix} 0.0093F^2 - 0.3453F \\ +5.9675 \end{bmatrix}$$

$$= 1038 \times 0.0141 \times 0.2 \begin{bmatrix} 0.0093 \times 400 - 0.3453 \times 20 \\ +5.9675 \end{bmatrix}$$

$$= 2.928 \times [2.7815]$$

$$= 34.1 \, \text{J/cm}^2 \left(8.144 \, \text{cal/cm}^2\right)$$

D.3.4 Reference. The equations for this section were derived in the IEEE paper by R. L. Doughty, T. E. Neal, and H. L. Floyd, II, "Predicting Incident Energy to Better Manage the Electric Arc Hazard on 600 V Power Distribution Systems."

D.4 IEEE 1584-2018 Calculation Method.

N **D.4.1 Introduction.** This section provides a summary of the scope and purpose of IEEE 1584-2018, *Guide for Performing Arc Flash Hazard Calculations,* and it also provides an overview of the model range of parameters. Readers are encouraged to consult IEEE 1584-2018 for further information and detailed guidelines for proper application of the standard.

IEEE 1584-2018 is a revision of IEEE 1584-2002 as amended by IEEE 1584a-2004 and IEEE 1584b-2011.

The scope and purpose of IEEE 1584-2018 are in D.4.2 and D.4.3.

N **D.4.2 Scope.** This guide provides models and an analytical process to enable calculation of the predicted incident thermal energy and the arc-flash boundary (AFB). The process covers a collection of applicable field data, consideration of power system operating scenarios, and calculation parameters. Applications include electrical equipment and conductors for three-phase alternating current (ac) voltages from 208 volts to 15 kV. Calculations for single-phase ac systems and direct current (dc) systems are not a part of this guide, but some guidance and references are provided for those applications. Recommendations for personal protective equipment (PPE) to mitigate arc-flash hazards are not included in this guide.

N **D.4.3 Purpose.** The purpose of the guide is to enable qualified person(s) to analyze power systems for the purpose of calculating the incident energy (IE) to which employees could be exposed during operations and maintenance work. Contractors and facility owners can use this information to provide appropriate protection for employees in accordance with the requirements of applicable electrical workplace safety standards.

The new arc-flash model is a result of the IEEE/NFPA Arc-Flash Phenomena Collaborative Research Project and is based on over 1800 tests. The tests were performed at five different testing facilities over a 6-year period to ensure consistency and repeatability.

N D.4.4 Range of the Model. The range of the IEEE 1584-2018 model is provided in Table D.4.4.

N D.4.5 Comparison with IEEE 1584-2002. The following are differences between the IEEE 1584-2018 and the IEEE 1584-2002 arc flash models:

(1) The IEEE 1584-2002 arc-flash model was based on approximately 300 tests.
(2) The IEEE 1584-2018 model was based on over 1800 tests.
(3) IEEE 1584-2002 used two configurations.
(4) IEEE 1584-2018 includes five configurations.
(5) Five different labs were used for performing the tests.
(6) IEEE 1584-2002 test results were also used in new model.
(7) Based on the testing performed it was observed that sustainable arcs are possible but less likely in three-phase systems operating at 240 volts nominal or less with an available short-circuit current less than 2000 amperes.

N D.4.6 Electrode Configuration. The orientation and arrangement of the electrodes used in the testing performed for the model development.

The following electrode configurations (test arrangements) in Table D.4.6 are defined and utilized in the incident energy model:

(1) VCB: Vertical conductors/electrodes inside a metal box/enclosure
(2) VCBB: Vertical conductors/electrodes terminated in an insulating barrier inside a metal box/enclosure
(3) HCB: Horizontal conductors/electrodes inside a metal box/enclosure
(4) VOA: Vertical conductors/electrodes in open air
(5) HOA: Horizontal conductors/electrodes in open air

N D.4.7 Enclosure Size Correction Factor. The VCB, VCBB, and HCB equations were normalized for a 508 mm × 508 mm × 508 mm (20 in. × 20 in. × 20 in.) enclosure. This model provides instructions on how to adjust incident energy for smaller and larger enclosures using a calculated correction factor.

N D.4.8 Cautions and Disclaimers. As an IEEE guide, this document suggests approaches for conducting an arc-flash hazard analysis but does not contain any mandatory requirements that preclude alternate methods. Following the suggestions in this guide does not guarantee safety, and users should take all reasonable, independent steps necessary to reduce risks from arc-flash events.

This information is offered as a tool for conducting an arc-flash hazard analysis. It is intended for use only by qualified persons who are knowledgeable about power system studies, power distribution equipment, and equipment installation practices. It is not intended as a substitute for the engineering judgment and adequate review necessary for such studies.

This guide is based upon testing and analysis of the thermal burn hazard presented by incident energy. Due to the explosive nature of arc-flash incidents, injuries can occur from ensuing molten metal splatters, projectiles, pressure waves, toxic arc by-products, the bright light of the arc, and the loud noise produced. These other effects are not considered in this guide.

This guide is subject to revision as additional knowledge and experience is gained. IEEE, those companies that contributed test data, and those people who worked on the development of this standard make no guarantee of results and assume no obligation or liability whatsoever in connection with this information.

The methodology in this guide assumes that all equipment is installed, operated, and maintained as required by applicable codes, standards, and manufacturers' instructions, and applied in accordance with its ratings. Equipment that is improperly installed or maintained may not operate correctly, possibly increasing the arc flash incident energy or creating other hazards.

N Table D.4.4 Range of Input Parameters for IEEE 1584-2018

Input parameter	Range
Voltage (Voc)	208 volts to 15,000 volts 3-phase (line-to-line)
Bolted fault current (I_{bf}): 208 volts to 600 volts — low voltage (LV)	500 amperes to 106 000 amperes (rms symmetrical)
Bolted fault current (I_{bf}): 601 volts to 15,000 volts — medium voltage (MV)	200 to 65 000 A (rms symmetrical)
Gap (G): 208 volts to 600 volts	6.35 mm to 76.2 mm (0.25 in. to 3 in.)
Gap (G): 601 volts to 15,000 volts	19.05 mm to 254 mm (0.75 in. to 10 in.)
Working distance (D)	≥ 305 mm (12 in.)
Fault clearing time (T)	No limit
Maximum height	1244.6 mm (49 in.)
Maximum width	1244.6 mm (49 in.)
Minimum width	Four times the gap mm ($4 \times G$)
Opening area	1.549 m² (2401 in.²)
Frequency	50 Hz or 60 Hz

N Table D.4.6 Electrode Orientation and Configurations

E.C.	Standard	Orientation	Configuration	Termination
VOA	2002/2018	Vertical	Open air	Open air
VCB	2002/2018	Vertical	Metal enclosure	Open air
VCBB	2018	Vertical	Metal enclosure	Insulating barrier
HOA	2018	Horizontal	Open air	Open air
HCB	2018	Horizontal	Metal enclosure	Open air

D.5 Direct-Current Incident Energy Calculations.

D.5.1 Maximum Power Method. The following method of estimating dc arc flash incident energy that follows was published in the *IEEE Transactions on Industry Applications (see reference 2 of D.5.2)*. This method is based on the concept that the maximum power possible in a dc arc will occur when the arcing voltage is one-half the system voltage. Testing completed for Bruce Power *(see reference 3 of D.5.3)* has shown that this calculation is conservatively high in estimating the arc flash value. This method applies to dc systems rated up to 1000 volts.

[D.5.1]

$$I_{arc} = 0.5 \times I_{bf}$$
$$IE_m = 0.01 \times V_{sys} \times I_{arc} \times T_{arc} / D^2$$

where:
I_{arc} = arcing current, amperes
I_{bf} = system bolted fault current, amperes
IE_m = estimated dc arc flash incident energy at the maximum power point, cal/cm²
V_{sys} = system voltage, volts
T_{arc} = arcing time, sec
D = working distance, cm

For exposures where the arc is in a box or enclosure, it would be prudent to consider additional PPE protection beyond the values shown in Table 130.7(C)(15)(b).

D.5.2 Detailed Arcing Current and Energy Calculations Method. A thorough theoretical review of dc arcing current and energy was published in the *IEEE Transactions on Industry Applications*. Readers are advised to refer to that paper *(see reference 1)* for those detailed calculations.

References:

1. "DC-Arc Models and Incident-Energy Calculations," Ammerman, R.F.; et al.; *IEEE Transactions on Industry Applications*, Vol. 46, No.5.

2. "Arc Flash Calculations for Exposures to DC Systems," Doan, D.R., *IEEE Transactions on Industry Applications*, Vol. 46, No.6.

3. "DC Arc Hazard Assessment Phase II", Copyright Material, Kinectrics Inc., Report No. K-012623-RA-0002-R00.

D.5.3 Short Circuit Current. The determination of short circuit current is necessary in order to use Table 130.7(C)(15)(b). The arcing current is calculated at 50 percent of the dc short-circuit value. The current that a battery will deliver depends on the total impedance of the short-circuit path. A conservative approach in determining the short-circuit current that the battery will deliver at 25°C is to assume that the maximum available short-circuit current is 10 times the 1 minute ampere rating (to 1.75 volts per cell at 25°C and the specific gravity of 1.215) of the battery. A more accurate value for the short-circuit current for the specific application can be obtained from the battery manufacturer.

References:

1. IEEE 946, *Recommended Practice for the Design of DC Auxiliary Powers Systems for Generating Stations*.

Informative Annex E   Electrical Safety Program

This informative annex is not a part of the requirements of this NFPA document but is included for informational purposes only.

(See 110.5, Electrical Safety Program.)

E.1 Typical Electrical Safety Program Principles. Electrical safety program principles include, but are not limited to, the following:

(1) Inspecting and evaluating the electrical equipment
(2) Maintaining the electrical equipment's insulation and enclosure integrity
(3) Planning every job and document first-time procedures
(4) De-energizing, if possible *(see 120.5)*
(5) Anticipating unexpected events
(6) Identifying the electrical hazards and reduce the associated risk
(7) Protecting employees from shock, burn, blast, and other hazards due to the working environment
(8) Using the right tools for the job
(9) Assessing people's abilities
(10) Auditing the principles

E.2 Typical Electrical Safety Program Controls. Electrical safety program controls can include, but are not limited to, the following:

(1) The employer develops programs and procedures, including training, and the employees apply them.
(2) Employees are to be trained to be qualified for working in an environment influenced by the presence of electrical energy.
(3) Procedures are to be used to identify the electrical hazards and to develop job safety plans to eliminate those hazards or to control the associated risk for those hazards that cannot be eliminated.

(4) Every electrical conductor or circuit part is considered energized until proved otherwise.
(5) De-energizing an electrical conductor or circuit part and making it safe to work on is, in itself, a potentially hazardous task.
(6) Tasks to be performed within the limited approach boundary or arc flash boundary of exposed energized electrical conductors and circuit parts are to be identified and categorized.
(7) Precautions appropriate to the working environment are to be determined and taken.
(8) A logical approach is to be used to determine the associated risk of each task.

E.3 Typical Electrical Safety Program Procedures. Electrical safety program procedures can include, but are not limited to determination and assessment of the following:

(1) Purpose of task
(2) Qualifications and number of employees to be involved
(3) Identification of hazards and assessment of risks of the task
(4) Limits of approach
(5) Safe work practices to be used
(6) Personal protective equipment (PPE) involved
(7) Insulating materials and tools involved
(8) Special precautionary techniques
(9) Electrical single-line diagrams
(10) Equipment details
(11) Sketches or photographs of unique features
(12) Reference data

Informative Annex F   Risk Assessment and Risk Control

This informative annex is not a part of the requirements of this NFPA document but is included for informational purposes only.

F.1 Introduction to Risk Management. Risk management is the logical, systematic process used to manage the risk associated with any activity, process, function, or product including safety, the environment, quality, and finance. The risk management process and principles can be used by organizations of any type or size.

The following risk management principles can readily be applied to electrical safety. Risk management:

(1) Is an integral part of all organizational processes and decision making
(2) Is systematic, structured, and timely
(3) Is based on the best available information
(4) Takes human and cultural factors into account
(5) Is dynamic, iterative, and responsive to change
(6) Facilitates continual improvement of the organization

Informational Note: For more information on risk management principles see ISO 31000:2009, *Risk Management — Principles and Guidelines.*

The risk management process includes the following:

(1) Communication and consultation
(2) Establishing the risk assessment context and objectives
(3) Risk assessment
(4) Risk treatment
(5) Recording and reporting the risk assessment results and risk treatment decisions
(6) Monitoring and reviewing risks

Risk assessment is the part of risk management that involves the following:

(1) Identifying sources of risk
(2) Analyzing the sources of risk to estimate a level of risk
(3) Evaluating the level of risk to determine if risk treatment is required

(*See Figure F.1.*)

F.1.1 Occupational Health and Safety (OHS) Risk Management. The same logical, systematic process and the same principles apply to risk management in the OHS sphere of activity. However, it is more focused and the terminology more narrowly defined, as follows:

(1) The OHS objective is freedom from harm (i.e., injury or damage to health).
(2) Sources of risk are referred to as hazards.
(3) Analyzing and estimating the level of risk is a combination of the estimation of the likelihood of the occurrence of harm and the severity of that harm.
(4) The level of risk is evaluated to determine if it is reasonable to conclude that freedom from harm can be achieved or if further risk treatment is required.
(5) Risk treatment is referred to as risk control.

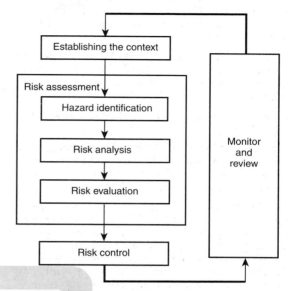

FIGURE F.1   Risk Management Process (Adapted from ISO 31000 figure 3).

Therefore, OHS risk assessment involves the following:

(1) Hazard identification: Find, list, and characterize hazards.
(2) Risk analysis: Sources, causes, and potential consequences are analyzed to determine the following:

   a. The likelihood that harm might result
   b. The potential severity of that harm
   c. Estimate the level of risk
(3) Risk evaluation: The level of risk is evaluated to determine if the objective of freedom from harm can reasonably be met by the risk control that is in place or is further risk control required?

F.2 Relationship to Occupational Health and Safety Management System (OHSMS). As discussed in Annex P, the most effective application of the requirements of this standard can be achieved within the framework of an OHSMS. Using a management system provides a methodical approach to health and safety by means of goal setting, planning, and performance measurement.

Risk management shares the six management system process elements of the following:

(1) Leadership. If any venture is to succeed it needs to be sponsored at the highest levels of the organization.
(2) Policy. The organization should articulate its vision and establish relevant, attainable goals.
(3) Plan. A plan is developed in line with the organization's vision and to achieve its goals. The plan must include mechanisms to measure and monitor the success of the plan.

(4) Do. The plan is executed.

(5) Check (Monitor). The success of the plan in achieving the organization's goals is continuously monitored.

(6) Act (Review). The measuring and monitoring results are compared to the organization's goals for the purposes of reviewing and revising goals and plans to improve performance.

As noted in F.1, risk management is iterative. The repeating nature of the management system plan-do-check-act (PDCA) cycle is intended to promote continuous improvement in health and safety performance.

Risk assessment fits into the "plan" and "do" stages of the PDCA cycle, as follows:

(1) Planning: Information used during the planning stage comes from sources that can include workplace inspections, incident reports, and risk assessments.

(2) Do: Risk assessment is an ongoing activity.

F.3 Hierarchy of Risk Control. The purpose of specifying and adhering to a hierarchy of risk control methods is to identify the most effective individual or combination of preventive or protective measures to reduce the risk associated with a hazard. Each risk control method is considered less effective than the one before it. Table F.3 lists the hierarchy of risk control identified in this and other safety standards and provides examples of each.

F.4 Hazard-Based Risk Assessment. In a hazard-based risk assessment, workplace hazards are identified and characterized for materials, processes, the worksite, and the environment. Activities that might be affected by those hazards are identified. The risk associated with each activity is analyzed for likelihood of harm and severity of harm. An organization uses this information to prioritize risk reduction decisions.

The information from hazard-based risk assessments is useful to organizations when designing, specifying, and purchasing electrical distribution equipment. Risk control is much more effective when it is applied at the beginning of the equipment or process lifecycle. Risk can be reduced by specifying "substitution" and "engineering" risk control methods that affect the likelihood of occurrence of harm or severity of harm.

F.5 Task-Based Risk Assessment. In a task-based risk assessment, a job is broken down into discrete tasks. Hazards are identified for each task (often referred to as task-hazard pairs). The risk associated with each hazard is analyzed and evaluated.

The task-based risk assessment is the most commonly used when performing a field level risk assessment.

F.6 Risk Assessment Methods. There are many risk assessment methods. The method or combination of methods should be chosen based on the following:

(1) The application

(2) The desired result

(3) The skill level of the persons performing the assessment

Some risk assessment methods include the following:

(1) Brainstorming. An open group discussion regarding hazards, the associated risk, and risk control methods can be used as part of pre-job planning and during a job briefing session.

(2) Checklists. A list of common hazards and possible control methods is a useful tool for pre-job planning and for job briefing purposes. See Annex I for an example of a job briefing and planning checklist.

(3) Risk assessment matrix. A risk assessment matrix is commonly used to quantify levels of risk. The matrix can be in a multilevel or a simple two-by-two format. See Figure F.6 for an example of a risk assessment matrix.

Informational Note: See ISO 31010, Risk management — *Risk assessment techniques*, and ANSI/AIHA Z10-2012, *Occupational Health and Safety Management Systems*, for further information regarding risk assessment methods.

N **F.7 Battery Risk Assessment.** Multiple hazards may be encountered when working on batteries (shock, arc flash, chemical, thermal). PPE selection should take into account all of the hazards depending on the task. The flow chart displayed in Figure F.7 will assist users to assess all hazards associated with work on batteries.

Table F.3 The Hierarchy of Risk Control Methods

Risk Control Method	Examples
(1) Elimination	Conductors and circuit parts in an electrically safe working condition
(2) Substitution	Reduce energy by replacing 120 V control circuitry with 24 Vac or Vdc control circuitry
(3) Engineering controls	Guard energized electrical conductors and circuit parts to reduce the likelihood of electrical contact or arcing faults
(4) Awareness	Signs alerting of the potential presence of hazards
(5) Administrative controls	Procedures and job planning tools
(6) PPE	Shock and arc flash PPE

Likelihood of Occurrence of Harm	Severity of Harm	
	Energy ≤ [Selected Threshold]	Energy > [Selected Threshold]
Improbable	Low	Low
Possible	Low	High

Legend

Likelihood of Occurrence of Harm	Severity of Harm
Improbable: Source of harm is adequately guarded to avoid contact with hazardous energy	Energy ≤ [Selected Threshold]: Level of hazardous energy insufficient to cause harm
Possible: Source of harm is not adequately guarded to avoid contact with hazardous energy	Energy > [Selected Threshold]: Level of hazardous energy insufficient to cause harm

Risk Evaluation

Identify the risk controls in place and evaluate the effectiveness of the controls. Prioritize actions taken to control risk based on the level of risk as follows:

Low: Risk Acceptable — Further risk control discretionary

High: Risk Unacceptable — Further risk control required before proceeding

Δ **FIGURE F.6   Example of a Qualitative Two-by-Two Risk Assessment Matrix.**

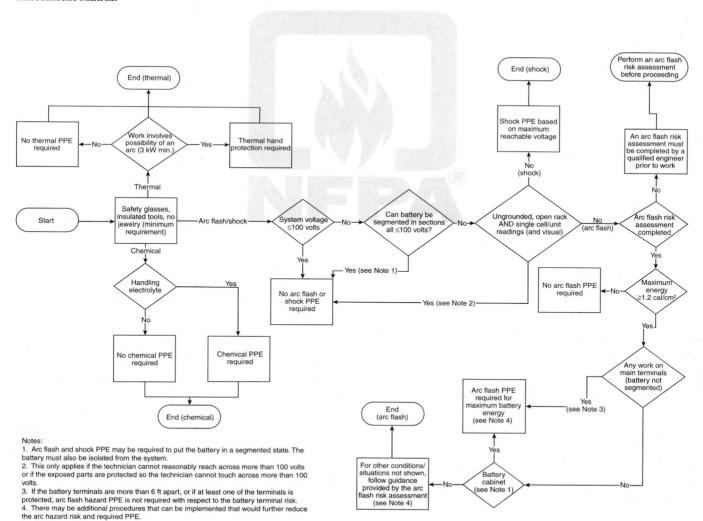

Notes:
1. Arc flash and shock PPE may be required to put the battery in a segmented state. The battery must also be isolated from the system.
2. This only applies if the technician cannot reasonably reach across more than 100 volts or if the exposed parts are protected so the technician cannot touch across more than 100 volts.
3. If the battery terminals are more than 6 ft apart, or if at least one of the terminals is protected, arc flash hazard PPE is not required with respect to the battery terminal risk.
4. There may be additional procedures that can be implemented that would further reduce the arc hazard risk and required PPE.

N **FIGURE F.7   Assessing Hazards Associated with Work on Batteries.**

Informative Annex G   Sample Lockout/Tagout Program

This informative annex is not a part of the requirements of this NFPA document but is included for informational purposes only.

Lockout is the preferred method of controlling personnel exposure to electrical energy hazards. Tagout is an alternative method that is available to employers. The sample program and procedures that follow are provided to assist employers in developing a lockout/tagout program and procedures that meet the requirements of Article 120 of *NFPA 70E.*The sample program and procedures can be used for a simple lockout/tagout or as part of a complex lockout/tagout. A more comprehensive procedure will need to be developed, documented, and used for the complex lockout/tagout.

LOCKOUT/TAGOUT PROGRAM

FOR [COMPANY NAME]

OR

TAGOUT PROGRAM FOR [COMPANY NAME]

1.0 Purpose. This procedure establishes the minimum requirements for lockout /tagout of electrical energy sources. It is to be used to ensure that conductors and circuit parts are disconnected from sources of electrical energy, locked (tagged), and tested before work begins where employees could be exposed to dangerous conditions. Sources of stored energy, such as capacitors or springs, shall be relieved of their energy, and a mechanism shall be engaged to prevent the reaccumulation of energy.

2.0 Responsibility. All employees shall be instructed in the safety significance of the lockout/tagout procedure. All new or transferred employees and all other persons whose work operations are or might be in the area shall be instructed in the purpose and use of this procedure. *[Name(s) of the person(s) or the job title(s) of the employee(s) with responsibility]* shall ensure that appropriate personnel receive instructions on their roles and responsibilities. All persons installing a lockout/tagout device shall sign their names and the date on the tag *[or state how the name of the individual or person in charge will be available].*

3.0 Preparation for Lockout/Tagout.

3.1 Review current diagrammatic drawings (or their equivalent), tags, labels, and signs to identify and locate all disconnecting means to determine that power is interrupted by a physical break and not de-energized by a circuit interlock. Make a list of disconnecting means to be locked (tagged).

3.2 Review disconnecting means to determine adequacy of their interrupting ability. Determine if it will be possible to verify a visible open point, or if other precautions will be necessary.

3.3 Review other work activity to identify where and how other personnel might be exposed to electrical hazards. Review other energy sources in the physical area to determine employee exposure to those sources of other types of energy. Establish energy control methods for control of other hazardous energy sources in the area.

3.4 Provide an adequately rated test instrument to test each phase conductor or circuit part to verify that they are de-energized *(see Section G.11.3)*. Provide a method to determine that the test instrument is operating satisfactorily.

3.5 Where the possibility of induced voltages or stored electrical energy exists, call for grounding the phase conductors or circuit parts before touching them. Where it could be reasonably anticipated that contact with other exposed energized conductors or circuit parts is possible, call for applying ground connecting devices.

4.0 Simple Lockout/Tagout. The simple lockout/tagout procedure will involve G.1.0 through G.3.0, G.5.0 through G.9.0, and G.11.0 through G.13.0.

5.0 Sequence of Lockout/Tagout System Procedures.

5.1 The employees shall be notified that a lockout/tagout system is going to be implemented and the reason for it. The qualified employee implementing the lockout/tagout shall know the disconnecting means location for all sources of electrical energy and the location of all sources of stored energy. The qualified person shall be knowledgeable of hazards associated with electrical energy.

5.2 If the electrical supply is energized, the qualified person shall de-energize and disconnect the electric supply and relieve all stored energy.

5.3 Wherever possible, the blades of disconnecting devices should be visually verified to be fully opened, or draw-out type circuit breakers should be verified to be completely withdrawn to the fully disconnected position.

5.4 Lockout/tagout all disconnecting means with lockout/tagout devices.

> Informational Note: For tagout, one additional safety measure must be employed, such as opening, blocking, or removing an additional circuit element.

5.5 Attempt to operate the disconnecting means to determine that operation is prohibited.

5.6 A test instrument shall be used. *(See G.11.3.)* Inspect the instrument for visible damage. Do not proceed if there is an indication of damage to the instrument until an undamaged device is available.

5.7 Verify proper instrument operation on a known source of voltage and then test for absence of voltage.

5.8 Verify proper instrument operation on a known source of voltage after testing for absence of voltage.

5.9 Where required, install a grounding equipment/conductor device on the phase conductors or circuit parts, to eliminate induced voltage or stored energy, before touching them. Where it has been determined that contact with other exposed energized conductors or circuit parts is possible, apply ground connecting devices rated for the available fault duty.

Shaded text = Revisions.   **Δ** = Text deletions and figure/table revisions.   • = Section deletions.   ***N*** = New material.

5.10 The equipment, electrical source, or both are now locked out (tagged out).

6.0 Restoring the Equipment, Electrical Supply, or Both to Normal Condition.

6.1 After the job or task is complete, visually verify that the job or task is complete.

6.2 Remove all tools, equipment, and unused materials and perform appropriate housekeeping.

6.3 Remove all grounding equipment/conductors/devices.

6.4 Notify all personnel involved with the job or task that the lockout/tagout is complete, that the electrical supply is being restored, and that they are to remain clear of the equipment and electrical supply.

6.5 Perform any quality control tests or checks on the repaired or replaced equipment, electrical supply, or both.

6.6 Remove lockout/tagout devices. The person who installed the devices is to remove them.

6.7 Notify the owner of the equipment, electrical supply, or both, that the equipment, electrical supply, or both are ready to be returned to normal operation.

6.8 Return the disconnecting means to their normal condition.

7.0 Procedure Involving More Than One Person. For a simple lockout/tagout and where more than one person is involved in the job or task, each person shall install his or her own personal lockout/tagout device.

8.0 Procedure Involving More Than One Shift. When the lockout/tagout extends for more than one day, it shall be verified that the lockout/tagout is still in place at the beginning of the next day. When the lockout/tagout is continued on successive shifts, the lockout/tagout is considered to be a complex lockout/tagout.

For a complex lockout/tagout, the person in charge shall identify the method for transfer of the lockout/tagout and of communication with all employees.

9.0 Complex Lockout/Tagout. A complex lockout/tagout plan is required where one or more of the following exist:

(1) Multiple energy sources (more than one)
(2) Multiple crews
(3) Multiple crafts
(4) Multiple locations
(5) Multiple employers
(6) Unique disconnecting means
(7) Complex or particular switching sequences
(8) Lockout/tagout for more than one shift; that is, new shift workers

9.1 All complex lockout/tagout procedures shall require a written plan of execution. The plan shall include the requirements in G.1.0 through G.3.0, G.5.0, G.6.0, and G.8.0 through G.12.0.

9.2 A person in charge shall be involved with a complex lockout/tagout procedure. The person in charge shall be at the procedure location.

9.3 The person in charge shall develop a written plan of execution and communicate that plan to all persons engaged in the job or task. The person in charge shall be held accountable for safe execution of the complex lockout/tagout plan. The complex lockout/tagout plan must address all the concerns of employees who might be exposed, and they must understand how electrical energy is controlled. The person in charge shall ensure that each person understands the electrical hazards to which they are exposed and the safety-related work practices they are to use.

9.4 All complex lockout/tagout plans identify the method to account for all persons who might be exposed to electrical hazards in the course of the lockout/tagout.

One of the following methods is to be used:

(1) Each individual shall install his or her own personal lockout or tagout device.
(2) The person in charge shall lock his/her key in a lock box.
(3) The person in charge shall maintain a sign-in/sign-out log for all personnel entering the area.
(4) Another equally effective methodology shall be used.

9.5 The person in charge can install locks/tags or direct their installation on behalf of other employees.

9.6 The person in charge can remove locks/tags or direct their removal on behalf of other employees, only after all personnel are accounted for and ensured to be clear of potential electrical hazards.

9.7 Where the complex lockout/tagout is continued on successive shifts, the person in charge shall identify the method for transfer of the lockout and the method of communication with all employees.

10.0 Discipline.

10.1 Knowingly violating the requirements of this program will result in [*state disciplinary actions that will be taken*].

10.2 Knowingly operating a disconnecting means with an installed lockout device (tagout device) will result in [*state disciplinary actions to be taken*].

11.0 Equipment.

11.1 Locks shall be [*state type and model of selected locks*].

11.2 Tags shall be [*state type and model to be used*].

11.3 The test instrument(s) to be used shall be [*state type and model*].

12.0 Review. This program was last reviewed on [date] and is scheduled to be reviewed again on [date] (not more than 1 year from the last review).

13.0 Lockout/Tagout Training. Recommended training can include, but is not limited to, the following:

(1) Recognition of lockout/tagout devices
(2) Installation of lockout/tagout devices
(3) Duty of employer in writing procedures
(4) Duty of employee in executing procedures
(5) Duty of person in charge
(6) Authorized and unauthorized removal of locks/tags
(7) Enforcement of execution of lockout/tagout procedures
(8) Simple lockout/tagout
(9) Complex lockout/tagout
(10) Use of single-line and diagrammatic drawings to identify sources of energy
(11) Alerting techniques
(12) Release of stored energy
(13) Personnel accounting methods
(14) Temporary protective grounding equipment needs and requirements
(15) Safe use of test instruments

Informative Annex H   Guidance on Selection of Protective Clothing and Other Personal Protective Equipment (PPE)

This informative annex is not a part of the requirements of this NFPA document but is included for informational purposes only.

H.1 Arc-Rated Clothing and Other Personal Protective Equipment (PPE) for Use with Arc Flash PPE Categories. Table 130.5(C), Table 130.7(C)(15)(a), Table 130.7(C)(15)(b), and Table 130.7(C)(15)(c) provide guidance for the selection and use of PPE when using arc flash PPE categories.

H.2 Simplified Two-Category Clothing Approach for Use with Table 130.7(C)(15)(a), Table 130.7(C)(15)(b), and Table 130.7(C)(15)(c). The use of Table H.2 is a simplified approach to provide minimum PPE for electrical workers within facilities with large and diverse electrical systems. The clothing listed in Table H.2 fulfills the minimum arc-rated clothing requirements of Table 130.7(C)(15)(a), Table 130.7(C)(15)(b), and Table 130.7(C)(15)(c). The clothing systems listed in this table should be used with the other PPE appropriate for the arc flash PPE category *[see Table 130.7(C)(15)(c)]*. The notes to Table 130.7(C)(15)(a), Table 130.7(C)(15)(b), and Table 130.7(C)(15)(c) must apply as shown in those tables.

H.3 Arc-Rated Clothing and Other Personal Protective Equipment (PPE) for Use with Risk Assessment of Electrical Hazards. Table H.3 provides a summary of specific sections within the NFPA *70E* standard describing PPE for electrical hazards.

H.4 Conformity Assessment of Personal Protective Equipment (PPE).

H.4.1 Introduction. Section 130.7(C)(14) requires personal protective equipment (PPE) provided by a supplier or manufacturer to conform to appropriate product standards by one of three methods. Additional information for these conformity assessment methods can be found within ANSI/ISEA 125, *American National Standard for Conformity Assessment of Safety and Personal Protective Equipment*. ANSI/ISEA 125 establishes criteria for conformity assessment of safety and PPE that is sold with claims of compliance with product performance standards. ANSI/ISEA 125 contains provisions for data collection, product verification, conformation of quality and manufacturing production control, and roles and responsibilities of suppliers, testing organizations, and third-party certification organizations.

H.4.2 Level of Conformity. ANSI/ISEA 125 provides for three different levels of conformity assessment: Level 1, Level 2, and Level 3.

Level 1 conformity is where the supplier or manufacturer is making a self-declaration that a product meets all of the requirements of the standard(s) to which conformance is claimed. A supplier Declaration of Conformity for each product is required to be made available for examination upon request.

Level 2 conformity is where the supplier or manufacturer is making a self-declaration that a product meets all of the requirements of the standard(s) to which conformance is claimed, the supplier or manufacturer has a registered ISO 9001 Quality Management System or equivalent quality management system, and all testing has been carried out by an ISO 17025 accredited testing laboratory. A supplier Declaration of Conformity for each product is required to be made available for examination upon request.

Level 3 conformity is where the products are certified by an ISO 17065 accredited independent third-party certification organization (CO). All product testing is directed by the CO, and all changes to the product must be reviewed and retested if necessary. Compliant products are issued a Declaration of

Table H.2 Simplified Two-Category, Arc-Rated Clothing System

Clothing[a]	Applicable Situations
Everyday Work Clothing Arc-rated long-sleeve shirt with arc-rated pants (minimum arc rating of 8) *or* Arc-rated coveralls (minimum arc rating of 8)	Situations where a risk assessment indicates that PPE is required and where Table 130.7(C)(15)(a) and Table 130.7(C)(15)(b) specify arc flash PPE category 1 or 2[b]
Arc Flash Suit A total clothing system consisting of arc-rated shirt and pants and/or arc-rated coveralls and/or arc flash coat and pants (clothing system minimum arc rating of 40)	Situations where a risk assessment indicates that PPE is required and where Table 130.7(C)(15)(a) and Table 130.7(C)(15)(b) specify arc flash PPE category 3 or 4[b]

[a]Note that other PPE listed in Table 130.7(C)(15)(c), which include arc-rated face shields or arc flash suit hoods, arc-rated hard hat liners, safety glasses or safety goggles, hard hats, hearing protection, heavy-duty leather gloves, rubber insulating gloves, and leather protectors, could be required. The arc rating for a garment is expressed in cal/cm^2.

[b]The estimated available fault current capacities and fault clearing times or arcing durations are listed in the text of Table 130.7(C)(15)(a) and Table 130.7(C)(15)(b). For power systems with greater than the estimated available fault current capacity or with longer than the assumed fault clearing times, Table H.2 cannot be used and arc flash PPE must be determined and selected by means of an incident energy analysis in accordance with 130.5(G).

Table H.3 Summary of Specific Sections Describing PPE for Electrical Hazards

Shock Hazard PPE	Applicable Section(s)
Rubber insulating gloves and leather protectors, unless the requirements of ASTM F496 are met	130.7(C)(7)(a)
Rubber insulating sleeves as needed	130.7(C)(7)(a)
Class G or E hard hat as needed	130.7(C)(3)
Safety glasses or goggles as needed	130.7(C)(4)
Dielectric overshoes as needed	130.7(C)(8)
Incident Energy Exposures Greater than or Equal to 1.2 cal/cm² (5 J/cm²)	
Clothing: Arc-rated clothing system with an arc rating appropriate to the anticipated incident energy exposure	130.7(C)(1), 130.7(C)(2), 130.7(C)(6), 130.7(C)(9)(d)
Clothing underlayers (when used): Arc-rated or nonmelting untreated natural fiber	130.7(C)(9)(c), 130.7(C)(11), 130.7(C)(12)
Gloves: Exposures greater than or equal to 1.2 cal/cm²(5 J/cm²) and less than or equal to 8 cal/cm² (33.5 J/cm²): heavy-duty leather gloves Exposures greater than 8 cal/cm² (33.5 J/cm²): rubber insulating gloves with their leather protectors or arc-rated gloves	130.7(C)(7)(b), 130.7(C)(10)(d)
Hard hat: Class G or E	130.7(C)(1), 130.7(C)(3)
Face shield: Exposures greater than or equal to 1.2 cal/cm²(5 J/cm²) and less than or equal to 12 cal/cm² (50.2 J/cm²): Arc-rated face shield that covers the face, neck, and chin and an arc-rated balaclava or an arc-rated arc flash suit hood Exposures greater than 12 cal/cm² (50.2 J/cm²): arc-rated arc flash suit hood	130.7(C)(1), 130.7(C)(3), 130.7(C)(10)(a), 130.7(C)(10)(b), 130.7(C)(10)(c)
Safety glasses or goggles	130.7(C)(4), 130.7(C)(10)(c)
Hearing protection	130.7(C)(5)
Footwear: Exposures less than or equal to 4 cal/cm² (16.75 J/cm²): Heavy-duty leather footwear (as needed) Exposures greater than 4 cal/cm² (16.75 J/cm²): Heavy-duty leather footwear	130.7(C)(10)(e)

Conformity by the CO and products are marked with the CO's mark or label.

H.4.3 Equivalence. While there are three levels of conformity assessment described in ANSI/ISEA 125, the levels are not to be considered as equivalent. Users are cautioned that the level of rigor required to demonstrate conformity should be based on the potential safety and health consequence of using a product that does not meet a stated performance standard. A higher potential safety and health consequence associated with the use of a noncompliant product should necessitate a higher level of conformity assessment.

H.4.4 Supplier's Declaration of Conformity. A Declaration of Conformity should be issued by the supplier and made available for examination upon request from a customer, user, or relevant authority. The Declaration of Conformity should, at a minimum:

(1) List the supplier name and address.
(2) Include a product model number or other identification details.
(3) List the product performance standard or standards (designation and year) to which conformance is claimed.
(4) Include a statement of attestation.

(5) Be dated, written on supplier letterhead, and signed by an authorized representative. The name and title of the authorized representative should also be printed.

Additional information should include:

(1) The level of conformity followed
(2) Whether the ISO 17025 testing facility is an independent or in-house laboratory (owned or partially owned by an entity within the supplier's corporate structure or within the manufacturing stream for the applicable product, including subcontractors and sub-suppliers)
(3) Reference to the test report (title, number, date, etc.) that serves as the basis of determining conformity

For an example of a Supplier's Declaration of Conformity see Figure H.4.4.

H.4.5 References. ANSI/ISEA contains detailed information and guidance on the application of the different conformity assessment levels. Copies of ANSI/ISEA 125 are available free of charge by emailing the International Safety Equipment Association at ISEA@Safetyequipment.org and requesting a complimentary copy.

Shaded text = Revisions.   **Δ** = Text deletions and figure/table revisions.   • = Section deletions.   *N* = New material.

Supplier's Declaration of Conformity

No. _____

Issuer's name: _____

Issuer's address: _____

Object of the declaration: _____

_____

_____

The object of the declaration described above is in conformity with the following documents:

Documents No.	Title	Edition/Date of issue
_____	_____	
_____	_____	
_____	_____	

Additional information:

_____

_____

_____

Signed for and on behalf of:

_____

Place and date of issue

_____

(Name, function)   (Signature or equivalent authorized by the issuer)

FIGURE H.4.4   Supplier's Declaration of Conformity.

Informative Annex I   Job Briefing and Job Safety Planning Checklist

This informative annex is not a part of the requirements of this NFPA document but is included for informational purposes only.

Δ **I.1 Job Briefing Checklist.** Figure I.1 illustrates considerations for a job briefing checklist.

N **I.2 Job Safety Planning Checklist.** Figure I.2 illustrates considerations for a job safety planning checklist.

Identify
- ❏ Hazards
- ❏ Voltage levels involved
- ❏ Skills required
- ❏ Any "foreign" (secondary source) voltage source
- ❏ Any unusual work conditions
- ❏ Number of people needed to do the job
- ❏ Shock protection boundaries
- ❏ Available incident energy
- ❏ Potential for arc flash (Conduct an arc flash risk assessment.)
- ❏ Arc flash boundary
- ❏ Any evidence of impending failure?

Ask
- ❏ Can the equipment be de-energized?
- ❏ Are backfeeds of the circuits to be worked on possible?
- ❏ Is an energized electrical work permit required?
- ❏ Is a standby person required?
- ❏ Is the equipment properly installed and maintained?

Check
- ❏ Job plans
- ❏ Single-line diagrams and vendor prints
- ❏ Status board
- ❏ Information on plant and vendor resources is up to date
- ❏ Safety procedures
- ❏ Vendor information
- ❏ Individuals are familiar with the facility

Know
- ❏ What the job is
- ❏ Who else needs to know — Communicate!
- ❏ Who is in charge

Think
- ❏ About the unexpected event . . . What if?
- ❏ Lock — Tag — Test — Try
- ❏ Test for voltage — FIRST
- ❏ Use the right tools and equipment, including PPE
- ❏ Install and remove temporary protective grounding equipment
- ❏ Install barriers and barricades
- ❏ What else . . . ?

Prepare for an emergency
- ❏ Is the standby person CPR/AED trained?
- ❏ Is the required emergency equipment available? Where is it?
- ❏ Where is the nearest telephone?
- ❏ Where is the fire alarm?
- ❏ Is confined space rescue available?
- ❏ What is the exact work location?
- ❏ How is the equipment shut off in an emergency?
- ❏ Are the emergency telephone numbers known?
- ❏ Where is the fire extinguisher?
- ❏ Are radio communications available?
- ❏ Is an AED available?

Δ **FIGURE I.1   Sample Job Briefing Checklist.**

Job Safety Planning Checklist

Equipment:	
Task:	
Location:	
Qualified submitter:	Date:

Section A, General

Mark "Y" or "N" as appropriate

No.	Item	Yes	No	Instructions
1.	Is there justification for the energized work? a. Equipment operating at less than 50 volts b. Additional hazard or increased risk c. Infeasible to de-energize d. Normal operating condition			*If **No**, the equipment must be placed in an electrically safe working condition.* *If **Yes**, complete 1a, 1b, and 1c, and shock and arc flash risk assessments are required to determine the appropriate hazard controls.* *Proceed to Line 2.*
2.	Will the worker be exposed to energized parts?			*If **No**, a shock risk assessment is discretionary and completing Sections B and C is optional.* *Proceed to Line 3.*
3.	Is there an arc flash hazard?			*If **No**, arc flash risk assessment is discretionary and completing Sections D or E and F is optional.* *Proceed to Line 4.*
4.	Were any of the answers to Questions 3 or 4 yes?			*If **No**, further risk assessment is discretionary.* *If **Yes**, proceed to Line 5.*
5.	Did the arc flash risk assessment determine that additional protective measures are required?			*If **No**, completing Parts D or E and F is discretionary.* *If **Yes**, Part D or E is required to be completed.* *Proceed to Line 6.*
6.	Is the required working distance available?			*If **Yes**, proceed to Line 7.* *If **No**, additional risk assessment is required before completing Section D or E or performing any work.* *Proceed to Line 7.*

Section B, Shock Hazard Information
Use Table 130.4(D)(a) for ac system boundaries or Table 130.4(D)(b) for dc system boundaries

No.	Item			Instructions
7.	Voltage between phases: Limited approach boundary: Restricted approach boundary:			*Establish the shock boundaries.* *Proceed to Line 8.*

Section C, Shock Control Information

Mark "Y" or "N" as appropriate

No.	Item			Instructions
8.	Will the task require the worker to cross the restricted approach boundary?			*If **No**, shock protection controls are discretionary.* *Proceed to Section D or E as appropriate.* *If **Yes**, shock protection controls are required.* *Proceed to Line 9.*
9.	Will rubber insulating gloves and leather protectors be used for the task?			*If **Yes**, proceed to Line 10.* *If **No**, proceed to Line 11.*
10.	Minimum glove class required for insulating gloves			*Establish minimum glove class.* *Proceed to Line 11.*
11.	Will insulating blankets be used for the task?			*If **Yes**, proceed to Line 12.* *If **No**, proceed to Line 13.*
12.	Minimum voltage rating for insulating blankets			*Establish minimum voltage rating.* *Proceed to Line 13.*

© 2020 National Fire Protection Association

NFPA 70E (p. 1 of 2)

N **FIGURE I.2   Sample Job Safety Planning Checklist.**

Shaded text = Revisions.   Δ = Text deletions and figure/table revisions.   • = Section deletions.   *N* = New material.

70E–79

	Mark "Y" or "N" as appropriate		
13.	Are insulated or insulating hand tools required for the task?		If **Yes**, proceed to Line 14. If **No**, proceed to Section D or E as applicable.
14.			Identify the hand tools, including the minimum voltage rating required. Proceed to Section D or E as applicable.

Section D, Arc Flash Control Information — Incident Energy Analysis Method *Use information from incident energy study*		

15.	Incident energy: Working distance: Level of PPE: Minimum arc rating of clothing: Arc flash boundary:	**Include:** the arc flash boundary **and** at least one of the following: the incident energy and the working distance **or** the level of PPE **or** the minimum arc rating of clothing. Proceed to Section F.

Section E, Arc Flash Hazard Control Information — Arc Flash PPE Category Method *Use Table 130.5(C)(15)(a) for ac systems or Table 130.7(C)(15)(b) for dc systems*		

16.	Determine the estimated available fault current and clearing times for the task.		
	Available *fault* current:	Overcurrent device clearing time:	
	Mark "Y" or "N" as appropriate		
17.	Do the estimated available fault current and clearing times for the task exceed the maximum allowed by Table 130.7(C)(15)(a) or Table 130.7(C)(15)(b)?		If **Yes**, an incident energy analysis is required. If **No**, proceed to Line 18.
18.	Arc flash boundary:		Proceed to Line 19.
19.	Arc flash PPE category: Working distance:		Proceed to Line 20 and 21, Section F.

Section F, Arc-Rated Clothing and Other Arc Flash Protection Equipment Information	

20.	Minimum arc rating in cal/cm^2 for protective clothing and other PPE	Establish the required arc-rated clothing and other PPE.
21.		List the required arc-rated clothing and other arc flash PPE. **PPE Category Method:** Use 130.7(C)(15)(c) and Table 130.7(C)(15)(c). **Incident Energy Analysis Method:** Use 130.5(G) and Table 130.5(G).

Section G, Energy Source Controls	

22.		List all sources of electrical supply to the specific equipment. Include location and method to lock or tag. Include method to verify and test for absence of voltage. List temporary protective grounding equipment.

Section H, Work Procedures and Special Precautions	

23.		List specific work procedures required to complete the task. List any special precautions needed to safely complete the task (i.e., discharge time for capacitors).

     NFPA 70E (p. 2 of 2)

N   **FIGURE I.2**   *Continued*

Informative Annex J   Energized Electrical Work Permit

This informative annex is not a part of the requirements of this NFPA document but is included for informational purposes only.

J.1 Energized Electrical Work Permit Sample. Figure J.1 illustrates considerations for an energized electrical work permit.

ENERGIZED ELECTRICAL WORK PERMIT

PART I: TO BE COMPLETED BY THE REQUESTER:

Job/Work Order Number _____

(1) Description of circuit/equipment/job location: _____
_____

(2) Description of work to be done: _____

(3) Justification of why the circuit/equipment cannot be de-energized or the work deferred until the next scheduled outage:
_____
_____

_____   _____
Requester/Title   Date

PART II: TO BE COMPLETED BY THE ELECTRICALLY QUALIFIED PERSONS *DOING* THE WORK:

Check when complete

(1) Detailed description of the job procedures to be used in performing the above detailed work: ☐
_____

(2) Description of the safe work practices to be employed: _____ ☐
_____

(3) Results of the shock risk assessment: _____
   (a) Voltage to which personnel will be exposed _____ ☐

   (b) Limited approach boundary _____ ☐

   (c) Restricted approach boundary _____ ☐

   (d) Necessary shock, personal, and other protective equipment to safely perform assigned task ☐

(4) Results of the arc flash risk assessment: _____
   (a) Available incident energy at the working distance or arc flash PPE category _____ ☐

   (b) Necessary arc flash personal and other protective equipment to safely perform the assigned task ☐

   (c) Arc flash boundary _____ ☐

(5) Means employed to restrict the access of unqualified persons from the work area:_____ ☐

(6) Evidence of completion of a job briefing, including discussion of any job-related hazards:_____ ☐

(7) Do you agree the above-described work can be done safely?   ☐ Yes ☐ No (If *no*, return to requester.)

_____   _____
Electrically Qualified Person(s)   Date

_____   _____
Electrically Qualified Person(s)   Date

PART III: APPROVAL(S) TO PERFORM THE WORK WHILE ELECTRICALLY ENERGIZED:

_____   _____
Manufacturing Manager   Maintenance/Engineering Manager

_____   _____
Safety Manager   Electrically Knowledgeable Person

_____   _____
General Manager   Date

Note: Once the work is complete, forward this form to the site Safety Department for review and retention.

© 2020 National Fire Protection Association   NFPA 70E

Δ **FIGURE J.1   Sample Permit for Energized Electrical Work.**

Shaded text = Revisions.   **Δ** = Text deletions and figure/table revisions.   • = Section deletions.   *N* = New material.

J.2 Energized Electrical Work Permit. Figure J.2 illustrates items to consider when determining the need for an energized electrical work permit.

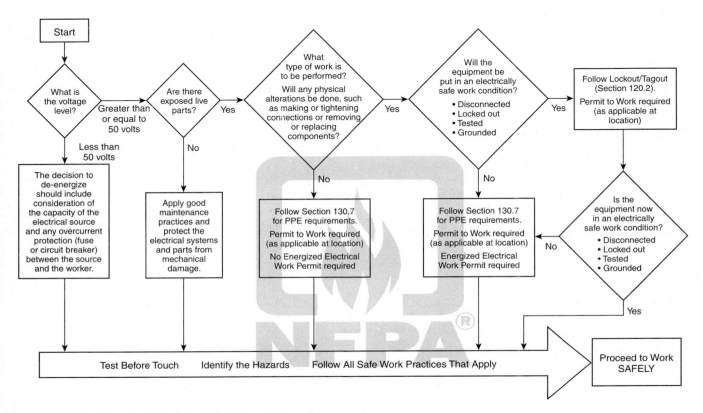

△ **FIGURE J.2** **Energized Electrical Work Permit Flow Chart.**

Informative Annex K   General Categories of Electrical Hazards

This informative annex is not a part of the requirements of this NFPA document but is included for informational purposes only.

K.1 General. Electrical injuries represent a serious workplace health and safety issue to electrical and non-electrical workers. Data from the U.S. Bureau of Labor Statistics (BLS) indicate that there were nearly 6000 fatal electrical injuries to workers in the United States from 1992 through 2012. BLS data also indicate that there were 24,100 non-fatal electrical injuries from 2003 through 2012. From 1992 to 2013, the number of fatal workplace electrical injuries has fallen steadily and dramatically from 334 in 1992 to 139 in 2013. However, the trend with non-fatal electrical injuries is less consistent. Between 2003 and 2009, non-fatal injury totals ranged from 2390 in 2003 to 2620 in 2009, with a high of 2950 injuries in 2005. Non-fatal injury totals between 2010 through 2012 were the lowest over this 10-year period, with 1890 non-fatal injuries in 2010, 2250 in 2011, and 1700 in 2012.

There are two general categories of electrical injury: electrical shock and electrical burns. Electrical burns can be further subdivided into burns caused by radiant energy (arc burns), burns caused by exposure to ejected hot gases and materials (thermal burns), and burns caused by the conduction of electrical current through body parts (conduction burns). In addition, hearing damage can occur from acoustic energy, and traumatic injury can be caused by toxic gases and pressure waves associated with an arcing event.

About 98 percent of fatal occupational electrical injuries are electrical shock injuries. A corporate case study examining electrical injury reporting and safety practices found that 40 percent of electrical incidents involved 250 volts or less and were indicative of a misperception of electrical safety as a high-voltage issue. In addition, electrical incidents once again were found to involve a large share of non-electrical workers, with approximately one-half of incidents involving workers from outside electrical crafts. Research of electrical fatalities in construction found that the highest proportion of fatalities occurred in establishments with 10 or fewer employees and pointed out that smaller employers could have fewer formal training requirements and less structured training in safety practices.

K.2 Electric Shock. Over 40 percent of all electrical fatalities in the U.S. involved overhead power line contact. This includes overhead power line fatalities from direct contact by a worker, contact through hand-carried objects, and contact through machines and vehicles. Comparing the ratio of total electrical fatalities to total electrical injuries (fatal and nonfatal), it was noticed that electrical injuries are more often fatal than many other injury categories. For example, from 2003 to 2009 there were 20,033 electrical injuries of which 1573 were fatalities. One worker died for every 12.74 electrical injuries. For the same period there were 1,718,219 fall injuries of which 5279 were fatalities — one worker died for every 325 injuries.

Of those, 1573 were electrical fatalities. A more detailed look at the demographics for 168 electrical fatalities in 2009 showed that 99 percent of deaths were the result of electrocution, and 70 percent occurred while the worker was performing a constructing, repairing, or cleaning activity.

K.3 Arc Flash. In the recently issued 29 CFR Subpart V, OSHA identified 99 injuries that involved burns from arcs from energized equipment faults or failures, resulting in 21 fatalities and 94 hospitalized injuries for the period January 1991 through December 1998.

Based on this data, OSHA estimated that an average of at least eight burn injuries from arcs occur each year involving employees doing work covered by OSHA rules, leading to 12 non-fatal injuries and two fatalities per year. Of the reports indicating the extent of the burn injury, 75 percent reported third-degree burns.

During the period involved, Federal OSHA only required non-fatal injuries to be reported when there were three or more workers hospitalized. OSHA found that there were six injuries for every fatality in California, which requires the reporting of every hospitalized injury.

Using that data, OSHA estimated that would be at least 36 injuries to every fatality, and probably many more. Also, many non-fatal electric shocks involve burns from associated electric arcs.

Starting January 1, 2015, Federal OSHA requires every hospitalized injury to be reported.

K.4 Arc Blast. The tremendous temperatures of the arc cause the explosive expansion of both the surrounding air and the metal in the arc path. For example, copper expands by a factor of 67,000 times when it turns from a solid to a vapor. The danger associated with this expansion is one of high pressures, sound, and shrapnel. The high pressures can easily exceed hundreds or even thousands of pounds per square foot, knocking workers off ladders, rupturing eardrums, and collapsing lungs. Finally, material and molten metal are expelled away from the arc at speeds exceeding 1120 km/hr (700 mph), fast enough for shrapnel to completely penetrate the human body.

K.5 Other Information. For additional information, the following documents are available:

Occupational Injuries From Electrical Shock and Arc Flash Events Final Report, by Richard Campbell, and David Dini, Sponsored by The Fire Protection Research Foundation, Quincy, MA.

Occupational Electrical Injuries in the US, 2003–2009, by James Cawley and Brett C. Banner, ESFI.

Technical paper ESW 2012-24 presented at IEEE ESW conference, *Arc Flash Hazards, Incident Energy, PPE Ratings and Thermal Burn Injury — A Deeper Look,* by Tammy Gammon, Wei-Jen Lee, and Ben Johnson.

Technical Paper ESW 2015-17 presented at IEEE ESW conference, OSHA Subpart V, *Electric Power and Distribution,* April 11, 2014.

Informative Annex L   Typical Application of Safeguards in the Cell Line Working Zone

This informative annex is not a part of the requirements of this NFPA document but is included for informational purposes only.

L.1 Application of Safeguards. This informative annex permits a typical application of safeguards in electrolytic areas where electrical hazards exist. Take, for example, an employee working on an energized cell. The employee uses manual contact to make adjustments and repairs. Consequently, the exposed energized cell and grounded metal floor could present an electrical hazard. Safeguards for this employee can be provided in the following ways:

(1) Protective boots can be worn that isolate the employee's feet from the floor and that provide a safeguard from the electrical hazard.

(2) Protective gloves can be worn that isolate the employee's hands from the energized cell and that provide a safeguard.

(3) If the work task causes severe deterioration, wear, or damage to personal protective equipment (PPE), the employee might have to wear both protective gloves and boots.

(4) A permanent or temporary insulating surface can be provided for the employee to stand on to provide a safeguard.

(5) The design of the installation can be modified to provide a conductive surface for the employee to stand on. If the conductive surface is bonded to the cell, a safeguard will be provided by voltage equalization.

(6) Safe work practices can provide safeguards. If protective boots are worn, the employee should not make long reaches over energized (or grounded) surfaces such that his or her elbow bypasses the safeguard. If such movements are required, protective sleeves, protective mats, or special tools should be used. Training on the nature of electrical hazards and proper use and condition of safeguards is, in itself, a safeguard.

(7) The energized cell can be temporarily bonded to ground.

L.2 Electrical Power Receptacles. Power supply circuits and receptacles in the cell line area for portable electric equipment should meet the requirements of 668.21 of *NFPA 70, National Electrical Code.* However, it is recommended that receptacles for portable electric equipment not be installed in electrolytic cell areas and that only pneumatic-powered portable tools and equipment be used.

Informative Annex M   Layering of Protective Clothing and Total System Arc Rating

This informative annex is not a part of the requirements of this NFPA document but is included for informational purposes only.

M.1 Layering of Protective Clothing.

M.1.1 Layering of arc-rated clothing is an effective approach to achieving the required arc rating when the layers have been tested together to determine the composite rating. The use of all arc-rated clothing layers will result in achieving the required arc rating with the lowest number of layers and lowest clothing system weight. Garments that are not arc rated should not be used to increase the arc rating of a garment or of a clothing system.

M.1.2 A total system of protective clothing can be determined to take credit for the protection provided by all the layers of clothing that are worn if tested as a combination. For example, to achieve an arc rating of 40 cal/cm^2 (167.5 J/cm^2), an arc flash suit with an arc rating of 40 cal/cm^2 (167.5 J/cm^2) could be worn over a cotton shirt and cotton pants. Alternatively, an arc flash suit with a 25 cal/cm^2 (104.7 J/cm^2) arc rating could be worn over an arc-rated shirt and arc-rated pants with an arc rating of 8 cal/cm^2 (33.5 J/cm^2) to achieve a total system arc rating of 40 cal/cm^2 (167.5 J/cm^2). This latter approach provides the required arc rating at a lower weight and with fewer total layers of fabric and, consequently, would provide the required protection with a higher level of worker comfort.

M.2 Layering Using Arc-Rated Clothing over Natural Fiber Clothing Underlayers.

M.2.1 Under some exposure conditions, natural fiber underlayers can ignite even when they are worn under arc-rated clothing.

M.2.2 If the arc flash exposure is sufficient to break open all the arc-rated clothing outerlayer or underlayers, the natural fiber underlayer can ignite and cause more severe burn injuries to an expanded area of the body. This is due to the natural fiber underlayers burning onto areas of the worker's body that were not exposed by the arc flash event. This can occur when the natural fiber underlayer continues to burn underneath arc-rated clothing layers even in areas in which the arc-rated clothing layer or layers are not broken open due to a "chimney effect."

M.3 Total System Arc Rating.

M.3.1 The total system arc rating is the arc rating obtained when all clothing layers worn by a worker are tested as a multi-layer test sample. An example of a clothing system is an arc-rated coverall worn over an arc-rated shirt and arc-rated pants in which all of the garments are constructed from the same arc-rated fabric. For this two-layer arc-rated clothing system, the arc rating would typically be more than three times higher than the arc ratings of the individual layers; that is, if the arc ratings of the arc-rated coverall, shirt, and pants were all in the range of 5 cal/cm^2 (20.9 J/cm^2) to 6 cal/cm^2 (25.1 J/cm^2), the total two-layer system arc rating would be over 20 cal/cm^2 (83.7 J/cm^2).

M.3.2 It is important to understand that the total system arc rating cannot be determined by adding the arc ratings of the individual layers. In a few cases, it has been observed that the total system arc rating actually decreased when another arc-rated layer of a specific type was added to the system as the outermost layer. The only way to determine the total system arc rating is to conduct a multilayer arc test on the combination of all of the layers assembled as they would be worn.

Informative Annex N Example Industrial Procedures and Policies for Working Near Overhead Electrical Lines and Equipment

This informative annex is not a part of the requirements of this NFPA document but is included for informational purposes only.

N.1 Introduction. This informative annex is an example of an industrial procedure for working near overhead electrical systems. Areas covered include operations that could expose employees or equipment to contact with overhead electrical systems.

When working near electrical lines or equipment, avoid direct or indirect contact. Direct contact is contact with any part of the body. Indirect contact is when part of the body touches or is in dangerous proximity to any object in contact with energized electrical equipment. The following two assumptions should always be made:

(1) Lines are "live" (energized).
(2) Lines are operating at high voltage (over 1000 volts).

As the voltage increases, the minimum working clearances increase. Through arc-over, injuries or fatalities could occur, even if actual contact with high-voltage lines or equipment is not made. Potential for arc-over increases as the voltage increases.

N.2 Overhead Power Line Policy (OPP). This informative annex applies to all overhead conductors, regardless of voltage, and requires the following:

(1) That employees not place themselves in close proximity to overhead power lines. "Close proximity" is within a distance of 3 m (10 ft) for systems up to 50 kV, and should be increased 100 mm (4 in.) for every 10 kV above 50 kV.
(2) That employees be informed of the hazards and precautions when working near overhead lines.
(3) That warning decals be posted on cranes and similar equipment regarding the minimum clearance of 3 m (10 ft).
(4) That a "spotter" be designated when equipment is working near overhead lines. This person's responsibility is to observe safe working clearances around all overhead lines and to direct the operator accordingly.
(5) That warning cones be used as visible indicators of the 3 m (10 ft) safety zone when working near overhead power lines.

Informational Note: "Working near," for the purpose of this informative annex, is defined as working within a distance from any overhead power line that is less than the combined height or length of the lifting device plus the associated load length and the required minimum clearance distance [as stated in N.2(1)]. Required clearance is expressed as follows:
Required clearance = lift equipment height or length + load length + at least 3 m (10 ft)

(6) That the local responsible person be notified at least 24 hours before any work begins to allow time to identify voltages and clearances or to place the line in an electrically safe work condition.

N.3 Policy. All employees and contractors shall conform to the OPP. The first line of defense in preventing electrical contact accidents is to remain outside the limited approach boundary. Because most company and contractor employees are not qualified to determine the system voltage level, a qualified person shall be called to establish voltages and minimum clearances and take appropriate action to make the work zone safe.

N.4 Procedures.

N.4.1 General. Prior to the start of all operations where potential contact with overhead electrical systems is possible, the person in charge shall identify overhead lines or equipment, reference their location with respect to prominent physical features, or physically mark the area directly in front of the overhead lines with safety cones, survey tape, or other means. Electrical line location shall be discussed at a pre-work safety meeting of all employees on the job (through a job briefing). All company employees and contractors shall attend this meeting and require their employees to conform to electrical safety standards. New or transferred employees shall be informed of electrical hazards and proper procedures during orientations.

On construction projects, the contractor shall identify and reference all potential electrical hazards and document such actions with the on-site employers. The location of overhead electrical lines and equipment shall be conspicuously marked by the person in charge. New employees shall be informed of electrical hazards and of proper precautions and procedures.

Where there is potential for contact with overhead electrical systems, local area management shall be called to decide whether to place the line in an electrically safe work condition or to otherwise protect the line against unintentional contact. Where there is a suspicion of lines with low clearance [height under 6 m (20 ft)], the local on-site electrical supervisor shall be notified to verify and take appropriate action.

All electrical contact incidents, including "near misses," shall be reported to the local area health and safety specialist.

N.4.2 Look Up and Live Flags. In order to prevent unintentional contact with all aerial lifts, cranes, boom trucks, service rigs, and similar equipment shall use look up and live flags. The flags are visual indicators that the equipment is currently being used or has been returned to its "stowed or cradled" position. The flags shall be yellow with black lettering and shall state in bold lettering "LOOK UP AND LIVE."

The procedure for the use of the flag follows.

(1) When the boom or lift is in its stowed or cradled position, the flag shall be located on the load hook or boom end.
(2) Prior to operation of the boom or lift, the operator of the equipment shall assess the work area to determine the location of all overhead lines and communicate this information to all crews on site. Once completed, the operator shall remove the flag from the load hook or boom and transfer the flag to the steering wheel of the vehicle. Once the flag is placed on the steering wheel, the operator can begin to operate the equipment.
(3) After successfully completing the work activity and returning the equipment to its stowed or cradled position, the operator shall return the flag to the load hook.

(4) The operator of the equipment is responsible for the placement of the look up and live flag.

N.4.3 High Risk Tasks.

N.4.3.1 Heavy Mobile Equipment. Prior to the start of each workday, a high-visibility marker (orange safety cones or other devices) shall be temporarily placed on the ground to mark the location of overhead wires. The supervisors shall discuss electrical safety with appropriate crew members at on-site tailgate safety talks. When working in the proximity of overhead lines, a spotter shall be positioned in a conspicuous location to direct movement and observe for contact with the overhead wires. The spotter, equipment operator, and all other employees working on the job location shall be alert for overhead wires and remain at least 3 m (10 ft) from the mobile equipment.

All mobile equipment shall display a warning decal regarding electrical contact. Independent truck drivers delivering materials to field locations shall be cautioned about overhead electrical lines before beginning work, and a properly trained on-site or contractor employee shall assist in the loading or off-loading operation. Trucks that have emptied their material shall not leave the work location until the boom, lift, or box is down and is safely secured.

N.4.3.2 Aerial Lifts, Cranes, and Boom Devices. Where there is potential for near operation or contact with overhead lines or equipment, work shall not begin until a safety meeting is conducted and appropriate steps are taken to identify, mark, and warn against unintentional contact. The supervisor will review operations daily to ensure compliance.

Where the operator's visibility is impaired, a spotter shall guide the operator. Hand signals shall be used and clearly understood between the operator and spotter. When visual contact is impaired, the spotter and operator shall be in radio contact. Aerial lifts, cranes, and boom devices shall have appropriate warning decals and shall use warning cones or similar devices to indicate the location of overhead lines and identify the 3 m (10 ft) minimum safe working boundary.

N.4.3.3 Tree Work. Wires shall be treated as live and operating at high voltage until verified as otherwise by the local area on-site employer. The local maintenance organization or an approved electrical contractor shall remove branches touching wires before work begins. Limbs and branches shall not be dropped onto overhead wires. If limbs or branches fall across electrical wires, all work shall stop immediately and the local area maintenance organization is to be called. When climbing or working in trees, pruners shall try to position themselves so that the trunk or limbs are between their bodies and electrical wires. If possible, pruners shall not work with their backs toward electrical wires. An insulated bucket truck is the preferred method of pruning when climbing poses a greater threat of electrical contact. Personal protective equipment (PPE) shall be used while working on or near lines.

N.4.4 Underground Electrical Lines and Equipment. Before excavation starts and where there exists reasonable possibility of contacting electrical or utility lines or equipment, the local area supervision (or USA DIG organization, when appropriate) shall be called and a request is to be made for identifying/marking the line location(s).

When USA DIG is called, their representatives will need the following:

(1) Minimum of two working days' notice prior to start of work, name of county, name of city, name and number of street or highway marker, and nearest intersection
(2) Type of work
(3) Date and time work is to begin
(4) Caller's name, contractor/department name and address
(5) Telephone number for contact
(6) Special instructions

Utilities that do not belong to USA DIG must be contacted separately. USA DIG might not have a complete list of utility owners. Utilities that are discovered shall be marked before work begins. Supervisors shall periodically refer their location to all workers, including new employees, subject to exposure.

N.4.5 Vehicles with Loads in Excess of 4.25 m (14 ft) in Height. This policy requires that all vehicles with loads in excess of 4.25 m (14 ft) in height use specific procedures to maintain safe working clearances when in transit below overhead lines.

The specific procedures for moving loads in excess of 4.25 m (14 ft) in height or via routes with lower clearance heights are as follows:

(1) Prior to movement of any load in excess of 4.25 m (14 ft) in height, the local health and safety department, along with the local person in charge, shall be notified of the equipment move.
(2) An on-site electrician, electrical construction representative, or qualified electrical contractor should check the intended route to the next location before relocation.
(3) The new site is to be checked for overhead lines and clearances.
(4) Power lines and communication lines shall be noted, and extreme care used when traveling beneath the lines.
(5) The company moving the load or equipment will provide a driver responsible for measuring each load and ensuring each load is secured and transported in a safe manner.
(6) An on-site electrician, electrical construction representative, or qualified electrical contractor shall escort the first load to the new location, ensuring safe clearances, and a service company representative shall be responsible for subsequent loads to follow the same safe route.

If proper working clearances cannot be maintained, the job must be shut down until a safe route can be established or the necessary repairs or relocations have been completed to ensure that a safe working clearance has been achieved.

All work requiring movement of loads in excess of 4.25 m (14 ft) in height are required to begin only after a general work permit has been completed detailing all pertinent information about the move.

N.4.6 Emergency Response. If an overhead line falls or is contacted, the following precautions should be taken:

(1) Keep everyone at least 3 m (10 ft) away.
(2) Use flagging to protect motorists, spectators, and other individuals from fallen or low wires.
(3) Call the local area electrical department or electric utility immediately.
(4) Place barriers around the area.
(5) Do not attempt to move the wire(s).
(6) Do not touch anything that is touching the wire(s).
(7) Be alert to water or other conductors present.

(8) Crews shall have emergency numbers readily available. These numbers shall include local area electrical department, utility, police/fire, and medical assistance.

(9) If an individual becomes energized, DO NOT TOUCH the individual or anything in contact with the person. Call for emergency medical assistance and call the local utility immediately. If the individual is no longer in contact with the energized conductors, CPR, rescue breathing, or first aid should be administered immediately, but only by a trained person. It is safe to touch the victim once contact is broken or the source is known to be de-energized.

(10) Wires that contact vehicles or equipment will cause arcing, smoke, and possibly fire. Occupants should remain in the cab and wait for the local area electrical department or utility. If it becomes necessary to exit the vehicle, leap with both feet as far away from the vehicle as possible, without touching the equipment. Jumping free of the vehicle is the last resort.

(11) If operating the equipment and an overhead wire is contacted, stop the equipment immediately and, if safe to do so, jump free and clear of the equipment. Maintain your balance, keep your feet together and either shuffle or bunny hop away from the vehicle another 3 m (10 ft) or more. Do not return to the vehicle or allow anyone else for any reason to return to the vehicle until the local utility has removed the power line from the vehicle and has confirmed that the vehicle is no longer in contact with the overhead lines.

Shaded text = Revisions. Δ = Text deletions and figure/table revisions. • = Section deletions. *N* = New material.

Informative Annex O   Safety-Related Design Requirements

This informative annex is not a part of the requirements of this NFPA document but is included for informational purposes only.

O.1 Introduction. This informative annex addresses the responsibilities of the facility owner or manager or the employer having responsibility for facility ownership or operations management to perform a risk assessment during the design of electrical systems and installations.

O.1.1 This informative annex covers employee safety-related design concepts for electrical equipment and installations in workplaces covered by the scope of this standard. This informative annex discusses design considerations that have impact on the application of the safety-related work practices only.

O.1.2 This informative annex does not discuss specific design requirements. The facility owner or manager or the employer should choose design options that eliminate hazards or reduce risk and enhance the effectiveness of safety-related work practices.

O.2 General Design Considerations.

O.2.1 Employers, facility owners, and managers who have responsibility for facilities and installations having electrical energy as a potential hazard to employees and other personnel should ensure that electrical hazard risk assessments are performed during the design of electrical systems and installations.

O.2.2 Design option decisions should facilitate the ability to eliminate hazards or reduce risk by doing the following:

(1)   Reducing the likelihood of exposure
(2)   Reducing the magnitude or severity of exposure
(3)   Enabling achievement of an electrically safe work condition

O.2.3 Incident Energy Reduction Methods. The following methods have proved to be effective in reducing incident energy:

(1)   Zone-selective interlocking. This is a method that allows two or more circuit breakers to communicate with each other so that a short circuit or ground fault will be cleared by the breaker closest to the fault with no intentional delay. Clearing the fault in the shortest time aids in reducing the incident energy.
(2)   Differential relaying. The concept of this protection method is that current flowing into protected equipment must equal the current out of the equipment. If these two currents are not equal, a fault must exist within the equipment, and the relaying can be set to operate for a fast interruption. Differential relaying uses current transformers located on the line and load sides of the protected equipment and fast acting relay.
(3)   Energy-reducing maintenance switching with a local status indicator. An energy-reducing maintenance switch allows a worker to set a circuit breaker trip unit to operate faster while the worker is working within an arc flash boundary, as defined in *NFPA 70E*, and then to set the circuit breaker back to a normal setting after the work is complete.

(4)   Energy-reducing active arc flash mitigation system. This system can reduce the arcing duration by creating a low impedance current path, located within a controlled compartment, to cause the arcing fault to transfer to the new current path, while the upstream breaker clears the circuit. The system works without compromising existing selective coordination in the electrical distribution system.
(5)   Energy-reducing line side isolation. This is equipment that encloses the line side conductors and circuit parts and has been listed to provide both shock and arc flash protection from events on the line side of a circuit breaker or switch.
(6)   Arc flash relay. An arc flash relay typically uses light sensors to detect the light produced by an arc flash event. Once a certain level of light is detected, the relay will issue a trip signal to an upstream overcurrent device.
(7)   High-resistance grounding. A great majority of electrical faults are of the phase-to-ground type. High-resistance grounding will insert an impedance in the ground return path and will typically limit the fault current to 10 amperes and below (at 5 kV nominal or below), leaving insufficient fault energy and thereby helping reduce the arc flash hazard level. High-resistance grounding will not affect arc flash energy for line-to-line or line-to-line-to-line arcs.
(8)   Current-limiting devices. Current-limiting protective devices reduce incident energy by clearing the fault faster and by reducing the current seen at the arc source. The energy reduction becomes effective for current above the current-limiting threshold of the current-limiting fuse or current limiting circuit breaker.
(9)   Shunt-trip. Adding a shunt-trip that is signaled to open from an open-fuse relay to switches 800 amperes and greater reduces incident energy by opening the switch immediately when the first fuse opens. The reduced clearing time reduces incident energy. This is especially helpful for arcing currents that are not within the current-limiting threshold of the three current-limiting fuses.

Δ **O.2.4 Additional Safety-by-Design Methods.** The following methods have proven to be effective in reducing risk associated with an arc flash or shock hazard:

(1)   Installing finger-safe components, covers, and insulating barriers reduces exposure to energized parts.
(2)   Installing disconnects within sight of each motor or driven machine increases the likelihood that the equipment will be put into an electrically safe work condition before work has begun.
(3)   Installing current limiting cable limiters can help reduce incident energy. Additionally, cable limiters can be used to provide short-circuit protection (and therefore incident energy reduction) for feeder tap conductors that are protected at up to 10 times their ampacity, a situation where the tap conductor can easily vaporize.
(4)   Installing inspection windows for noncontact inspection reduces the need to open doors or remove covers.
(5)   Installing a single service fused disconnect switch or circuit breaker provides protection for buses that would be unprotected if six disconnect switches are used.

(6) Installing metering to provide remote monitoring of voltage and current levels reduces exposure to electrical hazards by placing the worker farther away from the hazard.

(7) Installing Type 2 "no damage" current limiting protection to motor controllers reduces incident energy whenever the arcing current is within the current limiting threshold of the current-limiting fuse or current-limiting circuit breaker.

(8) Installing adjustable instantaneous trip protective devices and lowering the trip settings can reduce the incident energy.

(9) Installing arc-resistant equipment, designed to divert hot gases, plasma, and other products of an arc-flash out of the enclosure so that a worker is not exposed when standing in front of the equipment with all doors and covers closed and latched, reduces the risk of arc flash exposure.

(10) Installing provisions that provide remote racking of equipment, such as remote-controlled motorized remote racking of a circuit breaker or an MCC bucket, allows the worker to be located outside the arc-flash boundary. An extended length hand-operated racking tool also adds distance between the worker and the equipment, reducing the worker's exposure.

(11) Installing provisions that provide remote opening and closing of circuit breakers and switches could permit workers to operate the equipment from a safe distance, outside the arc flash boundary.

(12) Class C, D, and E special purpose ground fault circuit interrupters exist for circuits operating at voltages outside the range for Class A GFCI protection. See UL 943C for additional information.

Shaded text = Revisions. Δ = Text deletions and figure/table revisions. • = Section deletions. *N* = New material.

Informative Annex P   Aligning Implementation of This Standard with Occupational Health and Safety Management Standards

This informative annex is not a part of the requirements of this NFPA document but is included for informational purposes only.

Δ **P.1 General.** Injuries from electrical energy are a significant cause of occupational fatalities in the workplace in the United States. This standard specifies requirements unique to the hazards of electrical energy. By itself, however, this standard does not constitute a comprehensive and effective electrical safety program. The most effective application of the requirements of this standard can be achieved within the framework of a recognized health and safety management system. ANSI/AIHA Z10, *American National Standard for Occupational Health and Safety Management Systems,* and ISO 45001, *Occupational Health and Safety Management Systems — Requirements with Guidance for Use,* provides comprehensive guidance on the elements of an effective health and safety management system and are recognized standards. ANSI/AIHA Z10 and ISO 45001 are similar to other internationally recognized standards, such as ANSI/ISO 14001, *Environmental Management Systems — Requirements with Guidance for Use.* Some companies and other organizations have proprietary health and safety management systems that are aligned with the key elements of ANSI/AIHA Z10 and ISO 45001.

The most effective design and implementation of an electrical safety program can be achieved through a joint effort involving electrical subject matter experts and safety professionals knowledgeable about safety management systems.

Such collaboration can help ensure that proven safety management principles and practices applicable to any hazard in the workplace are appropriately incorporated into the electrical safety program.

This informative annex provides guidance on implementing this standard within the framework of ANSI/AIHA Z10 and ISO 45001 and other recognized or proprietary comprehensive occupational health and safety management system standards.

Informative Annex Q   Human Performance and Workplace Electrical Safety

This informative annex is not a part of the requirements of this NFPA document but is included for informational purposes only.

Q.1 Introduction. This annex introduces the concept of human performance and how this concept can be applied to workplace electrical safety.

Human performance is an aspect of risk management that addresses organizational, leader, and individual performance as factors that either lead to or prevent errors and their events. The objective of human performance is to identify and address human error and its negative consequences on people, programs, processes, the work environment, an organization, or equipment.

Studies by high-risk industries indicate that human error is often a root cause of incidents. The premise of this annex is that human error is similarly a frequent root cause of electrical incidents. In occupational health and safety terms, an incident is an occurrence arising in the course of work that resulted in or could have resulted in an injury, illness, damage to health, or a fatality (see ANSI/AIHA Z10-2012, *Definition of Incident*).

The hierarchy of risk control methods identified in this and other standards is:

(1) Eliminating the hazard
(2) Substituting other materials, processes, or equipment
(3) Using engineering controls
(4) Establishing systems that increase awareness of potential hazards
(5) Setting administrative controls, e.g., training and procedures, instructions, and scheduling
(6) Using PPE, including measures to ensure its appropriate selection, use, and maintenance

The purpose of these controls is to either reduce the likelihood of an incident occurring or to prevent or mitigate the severity of consequence if an incident occurs. No control is infallible. All of the controls are subject to errors in human performance, whether at the design, implementation, or use phase.

Human performance addresses managing human error as a unique control that is complementary to the hierarchy of risk control methods.

Q.2 Principles of Human Performance. The following are basic principles of human performance:

(1) People are fallible, and even the best people make mistakes.
(2) Error-likely situations and conditions are predictable, manageable, and preventable.
(3) Individual performance is influenced by organizational processes and values.
(4) People achieve high levels of performance largely because of the encouragement and reinforcement received from leaders, peers, and subordinates.
(5) Incidents can be avoided through an understanding of the reasons mistakes occur and application of the lessons learned from past incidents.

Q.3 Information Processing and Attention. The brain processes information in a series of interactive stages:

(1) Attention — where and to what we intentionally or unintentionally direct our concentration.
(2) Sensing — sensory inputs (hearing, seeing, touching, smelling, etc.) receive and transfer information.
(3) Encoding, storage, thinking — incoming information is encoded and stored for later use in decision making (i.e., what to do with information). This stage of information processing involves interaction between the working memory and long-term memory (capabilities, knowledge, past experiences, opinions, and perspectives).
(4) Retrieval, acting — taking physical human action based on the synthesis of attention, sensation, encoded information, thinking, and decision-making. In a workplace environment this would include changing the state of a component using controls, tools, and computers, including verbal statements to inform or direct others.

According to Rasmussen's model used to classify human error, workers operate in one or more of three human performance modes: rule-based mode, skill-based mode, and knowledge-based mode.

Note: See Rasmussen, J. (1983); Skills, rules, and knowledge; signals, signs, and symbols, and other distinctions in human performance models. *IEEE Transactions on Systems, Man, and Cybernetics*, (3), 257-266.

Reason's Human Performance Generic Error Modeling System is an extension of Rasmussen's model. An individual consciously or subconsciously selects a human performance mode based on his or her perception of the situation. This perception is usually a function of the individual's familiarity with a specific task and the level of attention (information processing) applied to accomplish the activity.

Note: See Reason, J. *Human Error.* Cambridge, UK: Cambridge University Press, 1990.

Most cognitive psychologists agree that humans have a limited pool of attentional resources available to divide up among tasks. This pool of shared attentional resources enables the mind to process information while performing one or sometimes multiple tasks. Some tasks require more attentional resources than others. The amount of attentional resource required to perform a task satisfactorily defines the mental workload for an individual and is inversely proportional to the individual's familiarity with the task. An increase in knowledge, skill, and experience with a task decreases the level of attentional resources required to perform that task and therefore decreases the level of attentional resource allocated to that task.

Critical points in activities when risk is higher (increased likelihood of harm or increased severity of harm, or both) require an increased allocation of attentional resources. Allocation at these critical points can be improved by training, procedures, equipment design, and teamwork.

Each human performance mode has associated errors. Awareness of which human performance mode the individual might be in helps identify the kind of errors that could be made and which error prevention techniques would be the most effective.

Q.4 Human Performance Modes and Associated Errors.

Q.4.1 Rule-Based Human Performance Mode.

Q.4.1.1 General. An individual operates in rule-based human performance mode when the work situation is likely to be one that he or she has encountered before or has been trained to deal with, or which is covered by a procedure. It is called the rule-based mode because the individual applies memorized or written rules. These rules might have been learned as a result of interaction at the workplace, through formal training, or by working with experienced workers.

The level of required attentional resources when in the rule-based mode fits between that of the knowledge- and skill-based modes. The time devoted to processing the information (reaction time) to select an appropriate response to the work situation is in the order of seconds.

The rule-based level follows an *IF* (symptom X), *THEN* (situation Y) logic. The individual operates by matching the signs and symptoms of the situation to some stored knowledge structure, and will usually react in a predicable manner.

In human performance theory, rule-based is the most desirable performance mode. The individual can use conscious thinking to challenge whether or not the proposed solution is appropriate. This can result in additional error prevention being integrated into the solution.

Not all activities guided by a procedure are necessarily executed in rule-based mode. An experienced worker might unconsciously default to the skill-based mode when executing a procedure that is normally done in the rule-based mode.

Q.4.1.2 Rule-Based Human Performance Mode Errors. Since the rule-based human performance mode requires interpretation using an "if-then" logic, misinterpretation is the prevalent type error mode. Errors involve deviating from an approved procedure, applying the wrong response to a work situation, or applying the correct procedure to the wrong situation.

Q.4.2 Knowledge-Based Human Performance Mode.

Q.4.2.1 General. A worker operates in knowledge-based human performance mode when there is uncertainty about what to do; no skill or rule is readily identifiable. The individual relies on their understanding and knowledge of the situation and related scientific principles and fundamental theory to develop an appropriate response. Uncertainty creates a need for information. To gather information more effectively, the individual's attentional resources become more focused. Thinking takes more effort and energy, and the time devoted to processing the information to select an appropriate response to the situation can be in the order of minutes to hours.

Q.4.2.2 Knowledge-Based Human Performance Mode Errors. The prevalent error when operating in knowledge-based mode is that decisions are often based on an inaccurate mental picture of the work situation. Knowledge-based activities require decision making based on diagnosis and problem-solving. Humans do not usually perform optimally in high-stress, unfamiliar situations where they are required to "think on their feet" in the absence of rules, routines, and procedures to handle the situation. The tendency is to use only information that is readily available to evaluate the situation and to become enmeshed in one aspect of the problem to the exclusion of all other considerations. Decision-making is erroneous if problem-solving is based on incomplete or inaccurate information.

Q.4.3 Skill-Based Human Performance Mode.

Q.4.3.1 General. A person is in skill-based mode when executing a task that involves practiced actions in a very familiar and common situation. Human performance is governed by mental instructions developed by either practice or experience and is less dependent on external conditions. The time devoted to processing the information is in the order of milliseconds. Writing one's signature is an example of skill-based performance mode. A familiar workplace procedure is typically performed in skill-based performance mode, such as the operation of a low-voltage molded case circuit breaker.

Q.4.3.2 Skill-Based Human Performance Mode Errors. The relatively low demand on attentional resources required when an individual is in skill-based human performance mode can create the following errors:

(1) Inattention: Skill-based performance mode errors are primarily execution errors involving omissions triggered by human variability, or not recognizing changes in task requirements or work conditions related to the task.

(2) Perceived reduction in risk: As familiarity with a task increases, the individual's perception of the associated risk is less likely to match actual risk. A perceived reduction in risk can create "inattentional blindness" and insensitivity to the presence of hazards.

Q.5 Error Precursors. Error precursors are situations when the demands of the task and the environment it is performed in exceed the capabilities of the individual(s) or the limitations of human nature. Error precursors can also be unfavorable conditions that increase the probability for error during a specific action. Error precursors can be grouped into four broad categories.

(1) Task demands — when specific mental, physical, or team requirements to perform a task either exceed the capabilities or challenge the limitations of the individual assigned to the task.

(2) Work environment — when general influences of the workplace, organizational, and cultural conditions affect individual performance.

(3) Individual capabilities — when an individual's unique mental, physical, and emotional characteristics do not match the demands of the specific task.

(4) Human nature — when traits, dispositions, and limitations common to all persons incline an individual to err under unfavorable conditions.

Table Q.5 provides a list of specific examples for each category.

When error precursors are identified and addressed then the likelihood of human error is reduced.

Q.6 Human Performance Tools.

Q.6.1 Application. Human performance tools reduce the likelihood of error when applied to error precursors. Consistent use of human performance tools by an organization will facilitate the incorporation of best practice work. The following are some human performance tools. See Table Q.5 for a list of these tools.

Table Q.5 Error Precursor Identification and Human Performance Tool Selection *(see Q.5 and Q.6.1)*

Error Precursors	Optimal Tool(s)	Human Performance Tools
Task Demands Time pressure (in a hurry) High workload (memory requirements) Simultaneous or multiple tasks Repetitive actions or monotony Critical steps or irreversible acts Interpretation requirements Unclear goals, roles, or responsibilities Lack of or unclear standards **Work Environment** Distractions/interruptions Changes/departures from routine Confusing displays or controls Workarounds/out of service instrumentation Obscure electrical supplies or configurations Unexpected equipment conditions Lack of alternative indication Personality conflicts **Individual Capabilities** Unfamiliar with, or first time performing task Lack of knowledge (faulty mental model) New technique not used before Imprecise communication habits Lack of proficiency or experience Indistinct problem-solving skills Unsafe attitudes for critical task Inappropriate values **Human Nature** Stress (limits attention) Habit patterns Assumptions Complacency/overconfidence Mind-set Inaccurate risk perception Mental shortcuts (biases) or limited short-term memory		**1 Pre-job briefing** Identify hazards, assess risk and select and implement risk controls from a hierarchy of methods **2 Job site review** Increased situational awareness **3 Post-job review** Identify ways to improve and best practices Peer check **4 Procedure use and adherence** Step-by-step procedure read, outcome understood Circle the task to be performed, check off each task as it is completed **5 Self-check with verbalization** Stop, Think, Act, Review (STAR) Verbalize intent before, during, and after each task **6 Three-way communication** Directives are repeated by receiver back to sender; receiver is acknowledged by sender Use of the phonetic alphabet for clarity **7 Stop when unsure** Stop and obtain further direction when unable to follow a procedure or process step or if something unexpected occurs Maintain a questioning attitude **8 Flagging and blocking** Identify (flag) equipment and controls that will be operated Prevent access (block) equipment and controls that should not be operated

Notes:

This table may be utilized when identifying workplace hazards. Identify the error precursors in the left-hand column. Select the optimal human performance tool or combination of tools from the right-hand column. List the selected tool(s) in the centre column beside the associated error. This table does not include all possible human performance tools; however, all tools listed can be applied to each error precursor.

Q.6.2 Job Planning and Pre-Job Briefing Tool *[see 110.5(I)].* Creating a job plan and conducting pre-job briefing assists personnel to focus on the performance of the tasks and to understand their roles in the execution of the tasks.

The following is a graded approach that can be used when job planning to identify error precursors and select an appropriate human performance tool, or combination of tools, proportionate to the potential consequences of error:

(1) Summarize the critical steps of the job that, if performed improperly, will cause irreversible harm to persons or equipment, or will significantly impact operation of a process.

(2) Anticipate error precursors for each critical step.

(3) Foresee probable and worst-case consequences if an error occurs during each critical step.

(4) Evaluate controls or contingencies at each critical step to prevent, catch, and recover from errors and to reduce their consequences.

(5) Review previous experience and lessons learned relevant to the specific task and critical steps.

If one or more human performance tools are identified, then each tool should be discussed regarding its advantages, disadvantages, and when and how it should be applied.

Q.6.3 Job Site Review Tool. Incorporating a job site review into job planning facilitates the identification of hazards and potential barriers and delays. A job site review can be performed any time prior or during work.

Q.6.4 Post-Job Review Tool. A post-job review is a positive opportunity to capture feedback and lessons learned from the job that can be applied to future jobs. The use of or lack of use of human performance tools should be incorporated into the review.

The pre-job briefing and the post-job review are effective communication tools.

Shaded text = Revisions. Δ = Text deletions and figure/table revisions. • = Section deletions. *N* = New material.

Q.6.5 Procedure Use and Adherence Tool. Adhering to a written step-by-step sequential procedure is a human performance tool. The worker should proactively read and understand the purpose, scope, and intent of all actions as written and in the sequence specified.

An accurate and current account of progress should be kept by marking each step in the procedure as it is completed. This ensures that if the procedure is interrupted before all the steps are completed, the job site or activity can be left in a safe state and the procedure can be resumed at the point it was interrupted.

If the procedure cannot be used as written, or if the expected result cannot be accurately predicted, then the activity should be stopped and the issues resolved before continuing.

An example of adhering to a written step-by-step sequential procedure is a switching sequence, wherein the sequential order of operation of electrical distribution equipment is identified and documented for the purposes of de-energizing and re-energizing.

Q.6.6 Self-Check with Verbalization Tool. The self-check with verbalization tool is also known by the acronym STAR — Stop, Think, Act, and Review. Before, during, and after performing a task that cannot be reversed, the worker should stop, think, and openly verbalize their actions. Verbalizing permits the individual's brain to slow down to their body speed. It has the effect of keeping the individual focused, thus enabling them to act and then review their actions.

Example: A worker has one more routine task to complete before the end of shift — to approach a group of motor control panels and close a circuit breaker in one of those panels. The error precursors are task demands (in a hurry) and human nature (complacency). If the worker verbalizes each step in the task and the expected outcome of each step, he or she is less likely to operate the wrong circuit breaker and will be prepared in the event that the outcome of an action does not match the expectation. For example, the worker self checks and verbalizes:

(1) I am at Panel 12 Bravo (12B).
(2) I am about to close Circuit Breaker 4 Bravo (4B).
(3) The pump motor heater indicator light will engage bright red on Panel 10 Bravo (10B).
(4) The pump motor should not start.
(5) If the pump motor starts then I will open Circuit Breaker 4 Bravo.
(6) I am now closing Circuit Breaker 4 Bravo.

Q.6.7 Three-Way Communication Tool. The three-way communication tool facilitates a mutual understanding of the message between the sender and receiver. After a directive or statement is made by the sender, it is repeated by the receiver to confirm the accuracy of the message.

When the message includes the use of letters, then whenever possible the letters should be communicated using the phonetic alphabet.

Example: A sender issues a directive over a radio communication device: "Close circuit breaker 4 Bravo." The receiver repeats the message: "I understand, close circuit breaker 4 Bravo." The sender validates that the proper response was understood: "That is correct" or "Affirmative."

Q.6.8 Stop When Unsure Tool. When a worker is unable to follow a procedure or process step, if something unexpected occurs or if the worker has a "gut feeling" that something is not right, then the worker should stop and obtain further direction. The "stop when unsure" tool requires that the worker maintain a questioning attitude at all times.

Phrases such as "I think" or "I'm pretty sure," whether verbalized or not, indicate that the worker is in knowledge-based mode and needs to transition to rule-based mode. This transition should be communicated to co-workers.

Q.6.9 Flagging and Blocking Tools *[see 130.7(E)].* Flagging is a method to ensure the correct component is manipulated or worked on at the required time under the required conditions. A flag could be a marker, label, or device.

It should be used when an error-likely situation or condition is present, such as one of the following:

(1) Similar or "look-alike" equipment
(2) Work on multiple components
(3) Frequent operations performed in a short period of time
(4) Interruption of process critical equipment

Blocking is a method of physically preventing access to an area or equipment controls.

Hinged covers on control buttons or switches, barricades, fences or other physical barriers, whether temporary or permanent, are examples of blocking tools.

Blocking can be used in conjunction with flagging.

Q.7 Human Performance Warning Flags.

Q.7.1 General. There are common process, organizational, supervisory, and worker performance weaknesses that serve as human performance warning flags. These warning flags should be identified by the organization and action should be taken to address the root cause.

Q.7.2 Program or Process. The following are program or process human performance warning flags:

(1) Risk management processes are over-relied on, instead of personal ownership and accountability for managing risk.
(2) Risk management processes are inefficient or cumbersome ("more" is often not better).

Q.7.3 Organizational Performance. The following are organizational human performance warning flags:

(1) Personnel in the organization tend to engage in consensus or group thinking, without encouraging counterview points.
(2) Personnel overly defer to managers and perceived experts.
(3) Activities with high risk are not assigned clear owners.
(4) Past success without adverse outcomes becomes the basis for continuing current practices.
(5) The organization assumes that risk management is healthy because a program or process was established (i.e., complacency exists).

Q.7.4 Supervisory Performance. The following are supervisory human performance warning flags:

(1) Delegation is lacking, with a few individuals relied on to make major decisions.

(2) Supervision is physically or mentally separated from the job site and is insufficiently aware of current conditions and attitudes.

(3) Personnel in the organization do not understand how risk is perceived and managed at the worker level.

(4) Past success without adverse outcomes becomes the basis for continuing current practices.

(5) Performance indicators are used to justify existing risk management strategies.

Q.7.5 Worker Performance. The following are worker human performance warning flags:

(1) Individuals or groups exhibit self-imposed production pressure.

(2) Work activities are considered routine.

(3) Individuals are quick to make risky judgments without taking the time to fully understand the situation.

(4) Past success without adverse outcomes becomes the basis for continuing current practices.

(5) Personnel take pride in their ability to work through or with levels of risk that could have been mitigated or eliminated.

(6) Risk is not communicated effectively up the company. Individuals assume that the next level of supervision knows or understands the risk involved or that there are insufficient resources to manage the risk.

(7) Problem reporting is not transparent. Individuals are not willing to report high-risk conditions.

Q.8 Workplace Culture.

Q.8.1 General. The reduction or elimination of electrical incidents requires that all members at the workplace cultivate and consistently exhibit a culture that supports the use of human performance tools and principles. Workers, supervisors, and managers must all work together to implement strong human performance practices.

Q.8.2 Workers. The safe performance of activities by workers is a product of mental processes influenced by factors related to the work environment, the task demands, and the capabilities of the worker. All need to take responsibility for their actions and strive to improve themselves, the task at hand, and the work environment. Five general practices that should be consistently demonstrated by workers include the following:

(1) Communication to support a consistent understanding

(2) Anticipation of error-likely situations and conditions

(3) Desire to improve personal capabilities

(4) Reports on all incidents (including "near-miss" incidents)

(5) A commitment to utilize human performance tools and principles

Q.8.3 Supervisors and Managers. Through their actions, supervisors focus worker and team efforts in order to accomplish a task. To be effective, supervisors must understand what influences worker performance. Supervisors promote positive outcomes into the workplace environment to encourage desired performance and results. Supervisors must demonstrate a passion for identifying and preventing human performance errors. They influence both individual and company performance in order to achieve high levels of workplace electrical safety. Five general practices that should be consistently demonstrated by supervisors include the following:

(1) Promote open communication

(2) Encourage teamwork to eliminate error-likely situations and conditions

(3) Seek out and eliminate broader company weaknesses that may create opportunity for error

(4) Reinforce desired workplace culture

(5) Recognize the value in preventing errors, reporting of near-miss incidents, and the utilization of human performance tools and principles

Q.8.4 The Organization. It is important that an organization's procedures, processes, and values recognize and accept that people make mistakes. The policies and goals of an organization influence worker and supervisor performance. Five general practices that should be consistently demonstrated by an organization include the following:

(1) Promote open communication

(2) Foster a culture that values error prevention and the use of human performance tools

(3) Identify and prevent the formation of error-likely situations and conditions

(4) Support continuous improvement and learning across the entire organization

(5) Establish a blame-free culture that supports incident reporting and proactively identifies and reacts appropriately to risk

Shaded text = Revisions. Δ = Text deletions and figure/table revisions.   • = Section deletions.   *N* = New material.

N

Informative Annex R Working with Capacitors

N **R.1 Introduction.** Capacitors have the ability to store electrical energy after the source power has been disconnected. While many systems with capacitors are built with bleed resistors that automatically discharge the stored energy within a set time, these systems can sometimes fail, leaving a thermal, shock, arc flash, or arc blast hazard. Some capacitor systems might not have built-in bleed resistors. This informative annex provides detailed guidance on how to properly assess the risk in working with capacitors and implement suitable controls.

N **R.2 Qualification and Training.**

N **R.2.1 Qualifications.** Employees who perform work on electrical equipment with capacitors that exceed the energy thresholds in 360.3 should be qualified persons as required in Chapter 1 and should be trained in, and familiar with, the specific hazards and controls required for safe work.

N **R.2.2 Unqualified Persons.** Unqualified persons should be trained in, and familiar with, any electrical safety-related practices necessary for their safety.

N **R.3 Shock Hazard.**

N **R.3.1 General.** The capacitor shock hazard to a person is an impulse shock with an exponential decay curve. The severity of the shock is related to the amount of energy (joules) delivered and the time in which the energy is delivered. Injuries from capacitor shock include severe reflex action, internal and external burns, and heart fibrillation. Reflex injury can occur at energy levels as low as 0.25 joules when the capacitor voltage is over the skin breakdown threshold (about 400 volts), resulting in a very rapid delivery of the energy. Reflex action can result in injuries from falling, involuntarily coming in contact with other hazards, tearing muscles, tendons, and ligaments, or dislocation of joints. Internal burn injuries to nervous system and other tissues can occur at energies as low as 10s of joules. Heart fibrillation can happen when the voltage exceeds 100 volts and the stored energy delivered exceeds 10 joules under certain circumstances. However, even without fibrillation, a high-voltage, high-energy shock can cause serious injuries, either directly or through reflex action, down to as low as 0.25 joules. Instances of temporary paralysis, loss of consciousness, hearing damage, temporary loss of eyesight, burns, and dislocated joints have been reported. [See Figure R.3.1(a) for a capacitive shock circuit and Figure R.3.1(b) for a capacitive discharge curve.]

N **R.3.2 Duration of Discharge.** The duration of a capacitive discharge shock is independent of voltage and is generally assumed to be three times the time constant of the shock circuit. After three time constants, the voltage is reduced by 95 percent, and the energy has been reduced by 99.25 percent. The time constant, τ, is equal to body shock pathway resistance times capacitance, as follows:

N

$$\tau = RC$$

[R.3.2]

N **R.3.3 Current Delivered.** The current delivered by the shock is independent of capacitance and is proportional to the initial peak voltage and inversely proportional to shock pathway resist-

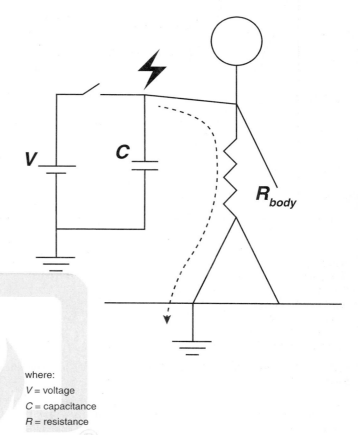

where:
V = voltage
C = capacitance
R = resistance

FIGURE R.3.1(a)   Capacitor Shock Circuit.

ance. Assuming that all of the stored energy is delivered in 3τ, the rms equivalent current can be expressed as follows:

N

$$I_{rms} = \frac{V_p}{R\sqrt{6}}$$

[R.3.3]

where:
I_{rms} = rms current
V_p = peak voltage
R = pathway resistance

N **R.3.4 Shock Pathway.** The shock pathway resistance depends on skin resistance, entry and exit locations, and internal body resistance. The severity of a capacitor discharge shock depends on the time of delivery (quickly or slowly) and the energy delivered. A capacitor disconnected from a live voltage source has only a finite amount of energy and can deliver that energy either quickly or slowly, depending on specific shock pathway resistance. As shock pathway resistance increases, the current lowers but the time to discharge also takes longer, and vice versa. Below 400 volts, skin breakdown is less likely and skin resistance (over 10,000 ohms for intact skin) will significantly reduce the shock current and extend discharge time. For punc-

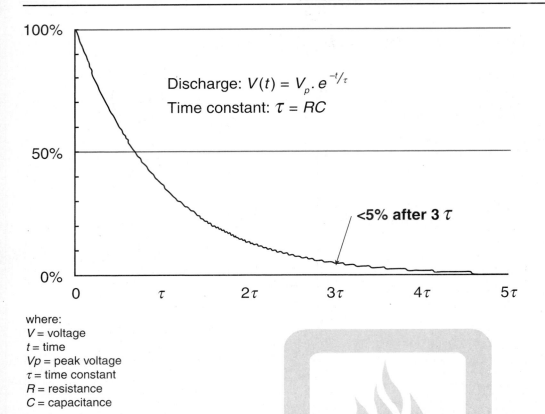

where:
V = voltage
t = time
Vp = peak voltage
τ = time constant
R = resistance
C = capacitance

FIGURE R.3.1(b)   Typical Exponential Discharge Characteristic of a Capacitor Through a Resistor.

tured, broken, or very wet skin, the contact resistance is 0 ohms to 100 ohms.

N R.3.5 Response to Shock Levels. For a given stored energy, there is a difference in response to whether it is a high-voltage, low-capacitance shock, or a low-voltage, high-capacitance shock. At high voltage and low capacitance, a hazardous shock will fully discharge nearly instantaneously (in microseconds) and could miss the vulnerable part of the heart cycle. However, the full energy is delivered to the person and there could be nerve or other tissue damage. At low voltage and high capacitance, the total discharge time can extend several seconds (multiple heart beats), behaving more like a dc shock. Both scenarios remain highly hazardous as fibrillation could still occur.

> Informational Note: For more information on impulse shock hazards, see IEC TS 60479-2, *Effects of Current on Humans and Livestock, Part 2, Special Aspects.*

N R.3.6 Reflex Hazard. Even when fibrillation does not occur, there remains the potential for serious bodily injury, especially above 400 volts. The reflex action to an impulse shock can be severe, causing persons to fall off of elevated platforms or ladders, knock a body part into nearby objects, or in some cases cause severe muscle clenching, temporary paralysis, or dislocated joints. This reflex hazard extends to lower energies even where fibrillation is unlikely. The lower threshold for hazardous reflex shocks is 0.25 joules for over 400 volts.

N R.3.7 Shock Hazard Thresholds. Capacitors connected to conductors or circuit parts operating at voltages equal to or

greater than 100 volts and containing a stored energy equal to or greater than 10 joules present a significant risk of shock and fibrillation. Below 10 joules, a significant risk of reflex action leading to injury could exist in the following situations:

(1) 100 volts–400 volts: if the stored energy is greater than 1 joule
(2) >400 volts: if the stored energy is greater than 0.25 joules

N R.4 Short-Circuit Hazard. Capacitors have the unique ability to discharge very rapidly in a shorted condition due to their low internal impedance. In ac power systems, faults typically occur on the order of milliseconds and are limited by transformer impedances. Battery faults take seconds or minutes to discharge. In contrast, capacitors have very little internal impedance and can fully discharge in microseconds, with very high discharge current. This current can cause heating of metals, arc flash injury, and arc blast injury, dependent on the stored energy in the capacitor. The shock injuries, including reflex and fibrillation, are discussed in R.3.7. Additional hazards that can result from capacitor energy include those discussed in R.4.1 through R.4.3.

N R.4.1 Thermal Hazard. At around 100 joules, a short through a metal object in contact with the worker, such as a ring or tool, can cause rapid heating and burns to the skin. Above 1 kJ, there can be substantial heating of metal, arcing, and magnetic forces causing mechanical deformation. Above 10 kJ, there is massive conductor melting, massive magnetic/mechanical motion, and an arc blast hazard.

Shaded text = Revisions.   **Δ** = Text deletions and figure/table revisions.   • = Section deletions.   ***N*** = New material.

N **R.4.2 Arc Flash Hazard.** At approximately 120 kJ, there exists sufficient stored energy to create an arc flash hazard (greater than 1.2 cal/cm^2 at a working distance of 18 in.). This is a conservative lower bound that assumes all of the stored energy has been converted to radiant heat. The threshold of 120 kJ could be lower for a capacitor in a box. There could be an additional contribution to the arc flash energy from an ac or dc source connected to the capacitor or capacitor bank.

N **R.4.3 Arc Blast Hazard.** Capacitors can have a significant arc blast hazard due to the very high short-circuit current involved. The effects of the acoustic shock wave can rupture eardrums and collapse lungs. While hearing protection should be used above 100 joules to mitigate against hearing damage, there is no PPE for protection against lung collapse, which becomes a hazard above 122 kJ.

N **R.5 Internal Rupture.**

N **R.5.1 High Currents.** When a capacitor is subjected to high currents, such as a short circuit condition, internal stresses could result in violent rupture of the capacitor enclosure.

N **R.5.2 Internal Failure.** When capacitors are used to store large amounts of energy, internal failure of one capacitor in a bank could result in the rupture and explosion of the failed capacitors when all other capacitors in the bank discharge into the fault. Fuses or inductive elements are often used to limit the fault current from a capacitor bank into a faulted individual capacitor. Improperly sized fuses or inductive elements for this application could explode.

N **R.5.3 Fire Hazard.** Rupture of a capacitor can create a fire hazard from ignition of the dielectric fluids. Dielectric fluids can release toxic gases when decomposed by fire or the heat of an electric arc.

N **R.6 Performing a Risk Assessment for Capacitors.**

N **R.6.1 Annex F.** The risk assessment process for capacitors can follow the overall risk management process found in Annex F. This risk assessment should be coordinated with the shock risk assessment of 130.4 and the arc flash risk assessment of 130.5.

N **R.6.2 Exposure to Stored Energy.** Whether there is an exposure to capacitor stored energy hazard should be determined. An exposure would exist when a conductor or circuit part that could potentially remain energized with hazardous stored energy is not properly guarded, enclosed, or insulated. All circuit parts that are electrically connected to a capacitor or capacitor bank could present this hazard. For example, a power factor correction bank could be in a completely separate enclosure; however, should the bank remained charged for some reason, the switchgear to which it is connected could also deliver the stored energy hazard.

N **R.6.3 Determining Shock Hazard.** The shock hazard should be determined using both the voltage and stored energy of the capacitor. A high-voltage capacitor is not a shock hazard below the energy threshold of 0.25 joules. Use the shock risk assessment process of 130.4 and the dc shock approach boundaries (for capacitors above 100 volts and 0.25 joules) and PPE ratings.

N **R.6.4 Determining Total Stored Energy.** The total capacitor stored energy (see R.8) of the system should be determined.

N **R.6.5 Determining Arc Flash.** The arc flash hazard (see R.9) should be determined. If stored energy is greater than 120 kJ, the arc flash incident energy and the arc flash boundary should be determined at the appropriate working distance. Appropriate arc flash PPE should be selected accordingly, but workers should always remain out of the arc blast lung protection boundary (see R.6.6).

N **R.6.6 Determining Arc Blast Hazard.** The arc blast hazard (see R.10) should be determined. Hearing protection should be used where the stored energy exceeds 100 joules. Where the stored energy exceeds 10 kJ, the hearing protection boundary should be calculated. If stored energy is above 122 kJ, determine the arc blast boundary for lung hazards. A lung collapse hazard could exist above 122 kJ. DO NOT ENTER THE LUNG PROTECTION BOUNDARY. There is no PPE for lung protection.

N **R.6.7 Determine the Test and Grounding Method.** (See R.11.)

N **R.6.8 Determining Discharge Time.** If capacitors are equipped with bleed resistors, or if using a soft grounding system, the required discharge wait time should be determined where applicable (see R.12). After the discharge time a hard ground stick or hard grounding system should be applied.

N **R.6.9 Written Discharge Procedure.** A written discharge procedure should be developed that captures all of the steps to place the equipment into an electrically safe work condition. Information about the amount of stored energy available, how long to wait after de-energization before opening the enclosure, how to test for absence of energy, and what to do if there is still stored energy present should be included.

N **R.6.10 Labeling.** Labeling the equipment with a hazard warning label (see R.15) should be considered so that qualified persons are made aware of the potential for stored energy and the need for a written discharge procedure. The maximum voltage and stored energy should be included.

N **R.7 Determining the Shock Hazard.**

N **R.7.1 Risk Assessment.** A shock risk assessment should be performed for capacitors exceeding the thresholds in 360.3 in accordance with 130.4. Shock approach boundaries are based on the peak voltage and the dc shock approach boundaries of Table 130.4(E)(b). Appropriately rated shock protection PPE, such as voltage-rated gloves and dielectric insulating sheeting, should be selected. The dc ratings for rubber insulated products should be used. (See ASTM D120, *Standard Specification for Rubber Insulating Gloves,* for dc ratings.) The restricted approach boundary should be used to assist in the selection of the length and voltage rating of the ground stick. Capacitors below the thresholds defined in 360.3 are not shock hazards, and 130.4 does not apply. This includes capacitors from 0 volts to 100 volts and less than 100 joules, capacitors 100 volts to 400 volts and less than 1 joule, and capacitors greater than 400 volts and less than 0.25 joules.

N **R.7.2 Shock PPE.** Shock protection PPE is required for all parts of the body that enter the restricted approach boundary for capacitor shock hazards defined in R.7.1. [See Table 130.4(E)(b).]

N **R.8 Determining Capacitor Stored Energy.**

N **R.8.1 Capacitor Stored Energy.** Determining capacitor stored energy could require detailed examination of schematics or manufacturer's information to properly determine both the peak voltage that will be applied to the capacitors and the total capacitance. The value of capacitance and the capacitor voltage rating can also be obtained from the labels on the capacitor, if done safely. Commercial capacitors often use unit labels of mF for millifarads and MF for microfarads.

N R.8.2 The stored energy in a capacitor is calculated as follows:

N [R.8.2]

$$E = \frac{1}{2}CV^2$$

where:
E = capacitive stored energy in joules
C = total capacitance in farads
V = peak voltage in volts

N R.8.3 Capacitor Calculations. Total capacitance of capacitor banks is calculated as follows:

(1)   For capacitors in parallel, add the capacitance as follows:

N [R.8.3a]

$$C_{total} = C_1 + C_2 + C_3 + ...$$

(2)   For capacitors in series, use the following:

N [R.8.3b]

$$\frac{1}{C_{total}} = \frac{1}{C_1} + \frac{1}{C_2} + \frac{1}{C_3} + ...$$

(3)   Capacitor banks used for power factor correction are often labeled with a kVAr value (kilovolt-amperes reactive) to facilitate power engineering calculations. Calculate the capacitance as follows:

N [R.8.3c]

$$C = \frac{Q}{2\pi f V^2}$$

where:
C = total capacitance in farads
Q = reactive power in VAr (volt-amperes reactive)
f = frequency in hertz
V = phase-to-phase voltage in volts rms
(4)   Long high-voltage coaxial cables can have significant capacitance, normally on the order of 45 pF/m–10 pF/m (1 picofarad = 1×10^{-12} F) for low-current applications, or 150 pF/m–450 pF/m for utility-grade, medium-voltage insulated cable. Manufacturer's specifications on capacitance per meter should be consulted.

N R.8.4 Voltage. For peak voltage, the voltage applied across the capacitors that would cause the maximum charge should be used. For disconnected capacitors in storage or for disposal, the capacitor rated voltage should be used.

N R.8.4.1 For dc systems, use the maximum available terminal voltage that could be applied to the capacitor by the system.

N R.8.4.2 For ac systems, nominal system voltage is normally expressed in volts rms (root mean square). For capacitor stored energy calculations, use the peak amplitude of the voltage, V_p, as follows:

N [R.8.4.2a]

$$V_{rms} = \frac{1}{\sqrt{2}}V_p = 0.707V_p$$

(1)   For single-phase ac systems, use peak ac voltage, as follows:

N [R.8.4.2b]

$$V_p = V_{rms}\sqrt{2}$$

(2)   For 3-phase wye-connected systems, use the peak phase-to-neutral ac voltage, as follows:

N [R.8.4.2c]

$$V_p = V_{\phi-N}\sqrt{2}$$

(3)   For 3-phase delta-connected systems, use the peak phase-to-phase ac voltage, as follows:

N [R.8.4.2d]

$$V_{cap} = V_{\phi-\phi}\sqrt{2}$$

Informational Note: For the same capacitance, a delta-connected system will have a total energy three times higher than a wye-connected system. Always check the configuration as design requirements vary.

N R.9 Determining the Arc Flash Hazard.

N R.9.1 Incident Energy. The maximum theoretical possible arc flash incident energy can be calculated by assuming that all of the stored energy is dissipated as radiant energy in a spherical expansion in open air. While this is unlikely, it helps set a lower bound of stored energy below which an arc flash hazard is unlikely.

N [R.9.1a]

$$IE_{open\ air} = \frac{Energy}{Area} = \frac{\frac{1}{2}CV^2}{4\pi r^2} = \frac{CV^2}{8\pi r^2}\ J/cm^2$$

Converting to cal/cm2 (1 cal = 4.184 joules) we obtain the following:

N [R.9.1b]

$$IE_{open\ air} = \frac{CV^2}{105.1r^2} = \frac{E}{52.6r^2}\ cal/cm^2$$

where:
IE = incident energy
E = energy
C = capacitance
V = voltage
r = radius

Shaded text = Revisions.   **Δ** = Text deletions and figure/table revisions.   • = Section deletions.   **N** = New material.

N R.9.2 Arc Flash Boundary. The arc flash boundary, where IE = 1.2 cal/cm^2, is then as follows:

N [R.9.2a]

$$AFB_{open\ air} = 0.126\sqrt{E}\,(cm) = 0.05\sqrt{E}\,(in.)$$

In a box, we can apply a three times factor over the open-air incident energy calculation, as follows:

N [R.9.2b]

$$IE_{box} = 3 \times IE_{open\ air}$$

N [R.9.2c]

$$AFB_{box} = \sqrt{3} \times AFB_{open\ air}$$

where:
AFB = arc flash boundary
IE = incident energy

Thus, the minimum stored energy (lower bound) required to obtain 1.2 cal/cm^2 at a working distance of 18 in. is roughly 44 kJ in a box or 120 kJ in open air. Extreme caution should be used with the open-air calculation, as the arc flash boundary can fall inside the lung protection boundary for arc blast. A better practice is to always use the box arc flash boundary as a minimum approach distance.

N R.10 Determining the Arc Blast Hazard.

N R.10.1 Hazard. The arc blast hazard is directly related to the instantaneous (initial) short circuit current. Since capacitors can discharge very rapidly, the shockwave generated by a capacitor discharge can cause barotrauma (overpressure injury) to persons in the area. The most sensitive organs are the ears, lungs, and brain. When a differential pressure across the eardrums exceeds around 20–35 kilopascals (3–5 psi), the eardrum can rupture. At 200 kilopascals (29 psi), lung damage can occur. The following formulas are used to estimate safe boundaries based on total stored energy, where "safe" is less than a 1 percent probability of eardrum rupture or lung injury:

N [R.10.1a]

$$R_{ear} = 49.29\sqrt[3]{\frac{E}{1000}} - 5.09$$

N [R.10.1b]

$$R_{lung} = 31.32\sqrt[3]{\frac{E}{1000}} - 155.45$$

where:
R_{ear} = eardrum rupture boundary (1 percent probability) in cm
R_{lung} = lung collapse boundary (1 percent probability) in cm
E = capacitor stored energy in joules

Informational Note: For more information about the derivation of these formulas, see Charles R. Hummer, Richard J. Pearson, and Donald H. Porschet, *"Safe Distances From a High-Energy Capacitor Bank for Ear and Lung Protection,"* Army Research Laboratory Report, ARL-TN-608, July 2014.

N R.10.2 Above 122 kJ. Above 122 kJ a lung collapse hazard can exist. It is not sufficient to wear arc flash PPE, as this will not protect against lung injury. Remain outside of the lung collapse boundary.

N R.10.3 Above 448 kJ. Above 448 kJ, the lung protection boundary will be greater than the arc flash boundary in open air calculated in R.9. A better practice is to always use the box arc flash boundary as a minimum approach distance. (See Figure R.10.3.)

N R.11 Selecting the Appropriate Test and Grounding Method.

N R.11.1 Method Selection. The method to safely discharge or verify discharge of a capacitor will vary depending on the degree of hazard. Low-voltage, low-energy capacitors can be verified de-energized with a properly rated test instrument meeting the requirements of 110.8 and/or hard grounded. At higher energy and voltage, soft grounding through a resistor could be needed to limit the discharge current. At very high energies (>100 kJ), manual testing or grounding can become a serious arc blast hazard, and remote metering and grounding should be performed.

N R.11.2 Bleed Systems. For systems with permanently installed bleed systems, testing for absence of voltage after the prescribed discharge time can be performed instead of applying grounds. Testing can also be performed as a means to verify absence of voltage after an automatically switched bleed system has grounded the system. In all cases, the test device must be rated for the system. (See Table R.11.9 for the appropriate test method.)

N R.11.2.1 Below 1000 volts and below 10 kJ, a properly rated, high-impedance digital voltmeter (DVM) can be used.

N R.11.2.2 Above 1000 volts and below 100 joules, a properly rated, high-impedance digital voltmeter (DVM) can be used with an approved attachment for measuring high-voltage dc on non-utility systems. On utility systems, a utility-grade, dc, resistive-type voltmeter must be used with a live-line tool.

N R.11.2.3 Above 1000 volts and between 100 joules and 100 kJ, a utility-grade, dc, resistive-type voltmeter can be used with a live-line tool.

N R.11.2.4 Above 100 kJ, engineered method can be used only for verifying absence of voltage.

N R.11.3 Hard Grounding. Hard grounding is the practice of shorting a capacitor from terminal to terminal and then directly to ground. Since the resistance is typically <0.1 ohm, the discharge time is rapid and the discharge current can be high. An intense spark and a loud noise can happen at higher energies. Above 100 joules there is a hearing damage hazard. The voltage reversal associated with using a hard ground can put excessive voltage stress on the capacitor. Since this is an equipment issue, check with the manufacturer for their recommendations.

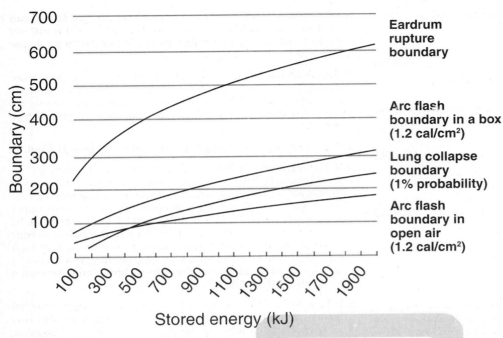

FIGURE R.10.3 Plot of Arc Flash and Blast Protection Boundaries.

N R.11.4 Soft Grounding. Soft grounding is the practice of discharging a capacitor through a resistor rated for the power. The resistor raises the time constant ($\tau = RC$) and reduces the peak discharge current ($I = V/R$) to safer levels. Soft discharge is necessary above 1000 joules.

N R.11.5 End of Discharge Time. At the conclusion of the specified discharge time, there is still voltage on the capacitors. A properly matched resistor and capacitor will reduce the voltage to less than 50 volts and the energy to less than 5 joules. At this point hard grounding is applied to fully short the capacitors to ground.

N R.11.6 Resistor Connection Point. Sometimes the grounding resistor is attached directly to the grounding stick. Other times, there are two separate grounding points built into the equipment itself. The grounding point labeled "High-Z" is the soft grounding point, where "High-Z" stands for high impedance. The grounding point labeled "Low-Z" is the hard grounding point, directly to ground. In this case the same ground stick is applied, first to the High-Z point, then to the Low-Z ground point. See Figure R.11.9.

N R.11.7 Lung Protection Boundary. The grounding method should keep all personnel clear of the lung protection boundary. For this reason, above 100 kJ, remote soft grounding is necessary.

N R.11.8 Ground Sticks. All ground sticks should meet the construction and periodic inspection requirements of R.16.

N R.11.9 Use of Table for Method Selection. See Table R.11.9, Figure R.11.9(a), and Figure R.11.9(b) for selection of the proper test and grounding methods.

Table R.11.9 Capacitor Test and Grounding Matrix to Establish Safe Discharge

	Test Method				Grounding Method		
	0–100 volts	100–1 kV	>1 kV		0–100 volts	100–1 kV	>1 kV
< 0.25 joules	Not applicable	Not applicable	Not applicable	< 0.25 joules	Not applicable	Not applicable	Not applicable
0.25–100 joules	Not applicable	DVM	DVM with HV adapter	0.25–100 joules	Not applicable	Hard ground ok	Hard ground ok
100 joules–1 kJ	DVM	DVM	HV utility grade dc voltmeter	100 joules–1 kJ	Hard ground ok	Hard ground ok	Hard ground ok
1 kJ–100 kJ	DVM	DVM	HV utility grade dc voltmeter	1 kJ–100 kJ	Soft ground then hard ground	Soft ground then hard ground	Soft ground then hard ground
>100 kJ	Engineered method	Engineered method	Engineered method	>100 kJ	Remote grounding only	Remote grounding only	Remote grounding only

Shaded text = Revisions. **Δ** = Text deletions and figure/table revisions. • = Section deletions. **N** = New material.

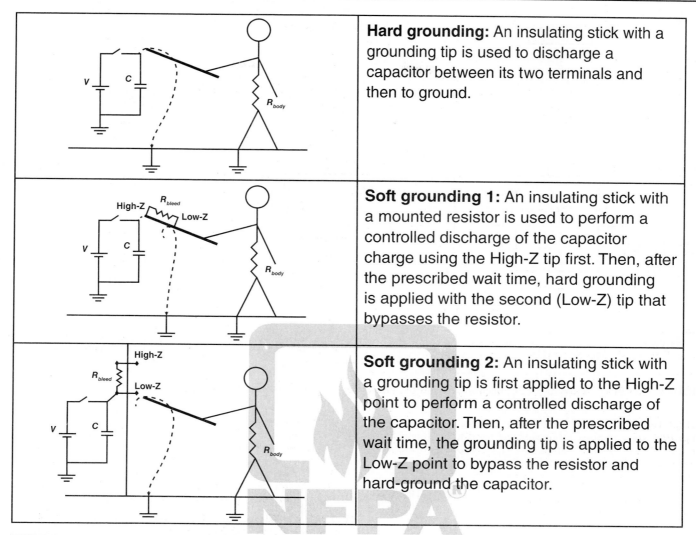

Hard grounding: An insulating stick with a grounding tip is used to discharge a capacitor between its two terminals and then to ground.

Soft grounding 1: An insulating stick with a mounted resistor is used to perform a controlled discharge of the capacitor charge using the High-Z tip first. Then, after the prescribed wait time, hard grounding is applied with the second (Low-Z) tip that bypasses the resistor.

Soft grounding 2: An insulating stick with a grounding tip is first applied to the High-Z point to perform a controlled discharge of the capacitor. Then, after the prescribed wait time, the grounding tip is applied to the Low-Z point to bypass the resistor and hard-ground the capacitor.

FIGURE R.11.9(a)   Illustration of Hard and Soft Grounding Examples

N **R.11.10 Other Considerations.** Other considerations are as follows:

(1) Charge transfer: Grounding capacitors in series may transfer charge between capacitors rather than discharge the stored energy. Special precaution should be taken in selecting the tools and sequence necessary to discharge capacitors connected in series. Improper grounding can result in moving charge around and not fully discharging to ground. Capacitor cases are not always grounded and should be considered charged unless otherwise determined.

(2) Dielectric absorption: Not all the energy in a capacitor is dissipated when it is short-circuited for a short time. Although the charge on the plates may be initially removed, dielectric polarization can cause charge to accumulate after the ground is removed. A voltage recharge of up to 10 percent can occur a few minutes after the grounding or shorting device has been removed. This can occur in capacitors with liquid dielectrics, such as an electrolytic capacitor, and in capacitors with solid dielectrics, such as polyethylene film capacitors.

(3) High-voltage capacitors can build a charge in the presence of high electric fields.

(4) A momentary hazardous voltage can exist at the moment of contact across the inductance of a few feet of the grounding cable of a ground stick at the moment of contact with a charged capacitor. This is why a worker should never hold the grounding cable during a discharge event.

N **R.12 Determining the Capacitor Discharge Time.**

N **R.12.1 Discharge Time.** The discharge time, T_d, of a capacitor is the time it takes to reduce to less than 100 volts. It is related to the time constant, τ. The discharge resistance can be permanently installed on the capacitors (e.g., a bleeder resistor), automatically switched in after power shutoff (e.g., a resistor dump bank), or applied through a soft grounding stick.

N **R.12.2 Voltages 1000 Volts and Less.** For voltages up to 1000 volts, it is sufficient to wait three times the time constant, or one minute, whichever is greater. That is because after 3τ, the residual voltage is less than 5 percent of the initial voltage.

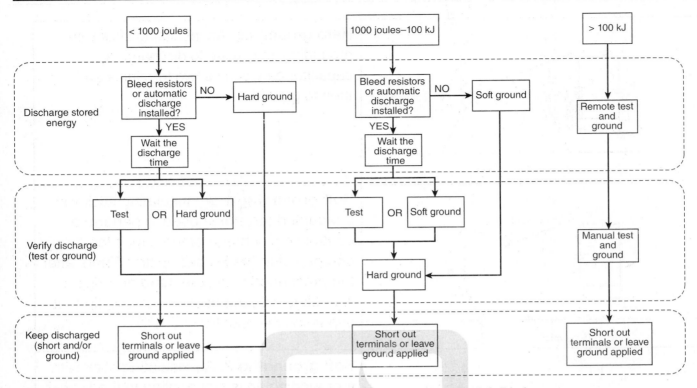

FIGURE R.11.9(b) Flowchart of Capacitor Test and Grounding Methods to Establish Safe Discharge

N **R.12.3 Voltages Greater Than 1000 Volts.** For voltages greater than 1000 volts, the discharge time will need to be longer than 3τ and should be calculated. Use the following formula to determine the minimum wait time:

N

$$\tau = RC \qquad \text{[R.12.3a]}$$

N

$$T_d = -\ln\left(\frac{100}{V_p}\right)\tau \qquad \text{[R.12.3b]}$$

where:
τ = time constant
R = discharge path resistance
C = total capacitance
T_d = discharge time (wait time)
V_p = peak voltage

N **R.13 Establishing an Electrically Safe Work Condition.**

N **R.13.1 Written Discharge Procedure.** Where a conductor circuit part is operating at or above 100 volts and 10 joules, a written discharge procedure (such as a complex LOTO procedure) should be used to document the necessary steps to place the equipment in an electrically safe work condition. The written discharge procedure should incorporate the results of the risk assessment performed in R.6 and specify the following at a minimum:

(1) Voltage in volts

(2) Energy in joules
(3) Specific steps to safely discharge the capacitor or verify that it is discharged
(4) Specific tool(s) (e.g., ground stick) or engineering system to discharge the capacitors, if necessary
(5) Specific test instruments (e.g., DVM) or engineered systems used to verify a de-energized state

N **R.13.2 Electrically Safe Work Condition.** In order to place the equipment with stored hazardous energy in an electrically safe work condition, a qualified person should follow the steps in 120.5 as well as the specific sequence outlined in the written discharge procedure. The process to remove stored energy in a capacitor is a part of the overall process to establish an electrical safe work condition in 120.5. These would then be as follows:

(1) Review the scope of work and the written discharge procedure. Determine all safe approach boundaries and necessary PPE and tools for the task.
(2) Perform a job briefing with the personnel involved and notify affected persons that the equipment will be de-energized.
(3) After properly interrupting the supply current, open the disconnecting device(s) for each source feeding the equipment.
(4) Wherever possible, visually verify that all blades of the disconnecting devices are fully open or that drawout-type circuit breakers are withdrawn to the fully disconnected position.
(5) Apply lockout/tagout devices in accordance with a documented and established policy, or use plug control on smaller equipment.

Shaded text = Revisions. Δ = Text deletions and figure/table revisions.   • = Section deletions.   *N* = New material.

(6) If bleed resistors or automatic discharge systems are applicable, wait the prescribed time for the capacitors to fully discharge to less than the thresholds in 360.3.

(7) Perform the test and ground method selected in R.11.

To ensure that recharging does not occur, all of the capacitor terminals should be connected together (shorted) and grounded with a non-insulated wire of sufficient gauge to withstand handling. For series capacitors these shorting wires should be attached across each individual capacitor and to case. For single capacitors or for a parallel capacitor bank, the grounding device should be permitted to be left hanging on the capacitor terminal during the work (e.g., a ground stick/hook).

N R.14 Storage and Disposal.

N R.14.1 Residual Charge. Any residual charge from capacitors should be removed by discharging the terminals before servicing or removal.

N R.14.2 Stored Capacitors. All uninstalled capacitors capable of storing energy exceeding the thresholds of 360.3 at their rated voltage should be short-circuited with a conductor of appropriate size.

N R.14.3 Capacitors Without Shorting Wire. When an uninstalled capacitor is discovered without a shorting wire attached to the terminals, it should be treated as energized and charged to its full rated voltage until determined otherwise. A qualified person should be contacted to determine the appropriate steps to safely discharge the capacitor.

N R.14.4 Change in Initial Capacitance. Large, high-voltage capacitors are often formed of a network of smaller capacitor elements connected inside a case. When such a capacitor develops an internal open circuit, it can retain a substantial charge internally even though the external terminals are short-circuited. Such a capacitor can be hazardous to transport because the damaged internal wiring can reconnect and discharge the capacitor through the short-circuiting wires. Any capacitor that shows a significant change in capacitance after a fault can have this problem. Action should be taken to reduce the risk associated with this hazard when it is discovered.

N R.15 Capacitor Hazard Labeling.

N R.15.1 Labeling. Electrical equipment operating at or above 100 volts and 10 joules should be field marked with a label containing all the following information:

(1) A warning about the potential for capacitive stored energy, with the word "WARNING" on an orange colored background

(2) Stored energy in joules and the maximum voltage for that stored energy

(3) The required wait time before opening the enclosure (the wait time needs to be greater than the discharge time)

(4) Date of the stored energy hazard analysis

(5) An instruction that a qualified person is necessary and that they should use a written discharge procedure

N R.15.2 Labeling should conform to the requirements of ANSI Z535.4, *Product Safety Signs and Labels.*

N R.16 Ground Sticks.

N R.16.1 Use of Ground Sticks. Ground sticks should be provided for qualified persons to safely discharge any residual stored energy contained in capacitor(s). The ground sticks should be designed, constructed, installed, and periodically inspected so that the full energy of a capacitor(s) can be safely discharged. See Table R.11.9 for selection guidance.

N R.16.2 Construction. Design and construction are as follows:

(1) Ground stick rod: When built of fiber reinforced plastic (FRP), the rod in the ground stick assembly should meet ASTM F711, *Standard Specification for Fiberglass-Reinforced Plastic (FRP) Rod and Tube Used in Live Line Tools*, specifications. Other insulating materials may be used provided they are of acceptable insulation and durability for the application. The stick should be long enough to be handled effectively and also to keep a person's hands out of the restricted approach boundary. This should include a non-moveable hand stop to remind the worker during use where to hold the ground stick.

(2) Ground stick tip: The ground stick connection to discharge points may be chain links, bare conductor, or solid copper bar in various geometries. The selection of the grounding tip should match the requirements of the intended application and ensure that all necessary circuit parts are fully discharged and grounded at the same time in order to avoid charge transfer. The grounding tips can be designed to remain applied (e.g., a hook) in order to safely prevent recharging from dielectric absorption. Alternatively, shorting straps may be applied while the grounding sticks are applied. Discharge points should be clearly marked and caution should be used to prevent transferring charge to other capacitors or reversing the charge on affected capacitors.

(3) Ground stick resistor: Soft grounding should be provided where stored energy exceeds 1000 joules. The resistor used to soft ground a capacitor(s) should be fully rated to handle power, voltage, and current. An engineering safety margin would be to calculate peak power, voltage and current, and double the resistor rating for each parameter. The resistor should be able to discharge the capacitor bank to less than 50 volts and less than 5 joules in less than 1 minute (less than 1000 volts) or less than 5 minutes (greater than 1000 volts). Ideally, the current should be limited to 500 amperes peak in order to reduce the magnetic force on the ground stick and its cable. This can require a discharge time longer than 5 minutes. Note that soft grounding is always followed by hard grounding to complete the discharge.

(4) Ground stick cable: The cable should be grounding or welding cable, flexible rope lay, soft drawn copper. The individual strands should not be larger than #30 AWG. Grounding cables have flexible, transparent elastomer or thermoplastic jackets primarily for mechanical protection of the conductor it covers and to allow visual examination of stranding degradation. Connections should be crimped according to manufacturer instructions. The lugs should be rated for the cables to be clamped. In permanent equipment installations the cable conductor size should be sized no smaller than #10 AWG stranded and capable of safely carrying the potential discharge current. For temporary or benchtop situations, the conductor should be capable of safely carrying any potential discharge current. Ground sticks should never be fused.

N R.16.3 Installation. Installation is as follows:

(1) Connection to building grounding system: Ground sticks should be connected to the building grounding electrode system where practicable. A qualified engineer should evaluate the connection point to the building grounding system to ensure the integrity of the ground stick system. This connection should be in a location accessible to and visible to the operator of the ground stick. Ground sticks should be connected such that impedance is less than 0.1 ohms to ground. High-Z ground sticks should be connected such that impedance is less than 0.1 ohms between the resistor and the ground connection.

(2) Operator access: The ground sticks should be permanently grounded and stored in the immediate area of the equipment in a manner that ensures they are used. The approach path to the equipment being grounded should be perpendicular to the equipment and clear of debris or obstructions. The ground stick operator will then always be facing the potential hazard and have the grounded conductor between them and the potentially energized equipment. For cases of capacitors in a field situation, or in portable equipment, a portable ground stick may be used. The ground stick must be effectively connected to the system ground, by a bolt or heavy-duty clamp, before opening the enclosure.

N R.16.4 Visual Inspection. Visual inspection is as follows:

(1) The ground stick should be visually inspected for defects before use each day.

(2) If any defect or contamination that could adversely affect the insulating qualities or mechanical integrity of the ground stick is present, the tool should be removed from service. All mechanical connections should be examined for loose connections. Ground sticks should have a hand guard that reduces the risk of improper hand position.

(3) If the defect or contamination exists on the grounding stick, then it should be replaced.

(4) If the defect or contamination exists on the cable, then it should be replaced or repaired and tested before return to service.

N R.16.5 Biennial Testing (every 2 years). A ground stick system places a grounded conductor at the end of the rod between the operator and the electrical hazard. The low impedance (Low-Z) ground stick system is not a live line tool, and there will not be a voltage potential at the end of the ground stick rod. High-impedance (High-Z) ground sticks can have a voltage potential at the end of the rod and should be treated as live line tools.

(1) For all ground sticks: The ground stick system should be tested to verify that impedance is less than 0.1 ohms to ground. This test should be performed annually when it is located outside or under any other adverse conditions.

(2) All High-Z ground stick insulating rods should be removed from service to be recertified to the ASTM F711, *Standard Specification for Fiberglass-Reinforced Plastic (FRP) Rod and Tube Used in Live Line Tools*, standard or equivalent.

(3) High-Z ground sticks with resistors: The resistor on the High-Z ground stick should be measured and compared to the specified value.

N R.17 References. IEC TS 60479-1, 4th Edition (2005), *Effects of Current on Human Beings and Livestock, Part 1, General Aspects*, Geneva, Switzerland.

IEC TS 60479-2, 3rd Edition (2007), *Effects of Current on Human Beings and Livestock, Part 2, Special Aspects*, Geneva, Switzerland.

DOE-HDBK-1092-2013, *DOE Handbook for Electrical Safety*, U.S. Department of Energy, Washington, DC.

Dalziel, Charles F., "A Study of the Hazards of Impulse Currents," *Transactions of the American Institute of Electrical Engineers. Part III: Power Apparatus and Systems*, Volume 72, Issue 2, 1953, DOI: 10.1109/AIEEPAS.1953.4498738.

Gordon, Lloyd B. and Cartelli, Laura, "A Complete Electrical Hazard Classification System and Its Application," IEEE *Transactions on Industry Applications*, Vol. 54, pp. 6554–6565, November/December 2018.

Hummer, Charles R., Pearson, Richard J., and Porschet, Donald H., "Safe Distances From a High-Energy Capacitor Bank for Ear and Lung Protection," Army Research Laboratory Report, ARL-TN-608, July 2014.

Richmond, D.R., Yelverton, J.T., Fletcher, E.R., and Phillips, YY, "Physical Correlates of Eardrum Rupture," *Annals of Otology Rhinology and Laryngology*, Vol. 109 (May 1989): 35–41.

Scott, Mark, "Working Safely with Hazardous Capacitors: Establishing Practical Thresholds for Risks Associated With Stored Capacitor Energy," IEEE *Industry Applications Magazine*, Vol. 25, Issue 3, 2019: 44–53.

Index

Sequence of Events for the Standards Development Process

Once the current edition is published, a Standard is opened for Public Input.

Step 1 – Input Stage

- Input accepted from the public or other committees for consideration to develop the First Draft
- Technical Committee holds First Draft Meeting to revise Standard (23 weeks); Technical Committee(s) with Correlating Committee (10 weeks)
- Technical Committee ballots on First Draft (12 weeks); Technical Committee(s) with Correlating Committee (11 weeks)
- Correlating Committee First Draft Meeting (9 weeks)
- Correlating Committee ballots on First Draft (5 weeks)
- First Draft Report posted on the document information page

Step 2 – Comment Stage

- Public Comments accepted on First Draft (10 weeks) following posting of First Draft Report
- If Standard does not receive Public Comments and the Technical Committee chooses not to hold a Second Draft meeting, the Standard becomes a Consent Standard and is sent directly to the Standards Council for issuance (see Step 4) or
- Technical Committee holds Second Draft Meeting (21 weeks); Technical Committee(s) with Correlating Committee (7 weeks)
- Technical Committee ballots on Second Draft (11 weeks); Technical Committee(s) with Correlating Committee (10 weeks)
- Correlating Committee Second Draft Meeting (9 weeks)
- Correlating Committee ballots on Second Draft (8 weeks)
- Second Draft Report posted on the document information page

Step 3 – NFPA Technical Meeting

- Notice of Intent to Make a Motion (NITMAM) accepted (5 weeks) following the posting of Second Draft Report
- NITMAMs are reviewed and valid motions are certified by the Motions Committee for presentation at the NFPA Technical Meeting
- NFPA membership meets each June at the NFPA Technical Meeting to act on Standards with "Certified Amending Motions" (certified NITMAMs)
- Committee(s) vote on any successful amendments to the Technical Committee Reports made by the NFPA membership at the NFPA Technical Meeting

Step 4 – Council Appeals and Issuance of Standard

- Notification of intent to file an appeal to the Standards Council on Technical Meeting action must be filed within 20 days of the NFPA Technical Meeting
- Standards Council decides, based on all evidence, whether to issue the standard or to take other action

Notes:

1. Time periods are approximate; refer to published schedules for actual dates.
2. Annual revision cycle documents with certified amending motions take approximately 101 weeks to complete.
3. Fall revision cycle documents receiving certified amending motions take approximately 141 weeks to complete.

Committee Membership Classifications[1,2,3,4]

The following classifications apply to Committee members and represent their principal interest in the activity of the Committee.

1. M *Manufacturer:* A representative of a maker or marketer of a product, assembly, or system, or portion thereof, that is affected by the standard.
2. U *User:* A representative of an entity that is subject to the provisions of the standard or that voluntarily uses the standard.
3. IM *Installer/Maintainer:* A representative of an entity that is in the business of installing or maintaining a product, assembly, or system affected by the standard.
4. L *Labor:* A labor representative or employee concerned with safety in the workplace.
5. RT *Applied Research/Testing Laboratory:* A representative of an independent testing laboratory or independent applied research organization that promulgates and/or enforces standards.
6. E *Enforcing Authority:* A representative of an agency or an organization that promulgates and/or enforces standards.
7. I *Insurance:* A representative of an insurance company, broker, agent, bureau, or inspection agency.
8. C *Consumer:* A person who is or represents the ultimate purchaser of a product, system, or service affected by the standard, but who is not included in (2).
9. SE *Special Expert:* A person not representing (1) through (8) and who has special expertise in the scope of the standard or portion thereof.

NOTE 1: "Standard" connotes code, standard, recommended practice, or guide.

NOTE 2: A representative includes an employee.

NOTE 3: While these classifications will be used by the Standards Council to achieve a balance for Technical Committees, the Standards Council may determine that new classifications of member or unique interests need representation in order to foster the best possible Committee deliberations on any project. In this connection, the Standards Council may make such appointments as it deems appropriate in the public interest, such as the classification of "Utilities" in the National Electrical Code Committee.

NOTE 4: Representatives of subsidiaries of any group are generally considered to have the same classification as the parent organization.

Submitting Public Input / Public Comment Through the Online Submission System

Following publication of the current edition of an NFPA standard, the development of the next edition begins and the standard is open for Public Input.

Submit a Public Input

NFPA accepts Public Input on documents through our online submission system at www.nfpa.org. To use the online submission system:

- Choose a document from the List of NFPA codes & standards or filter by Development Stage for "codes accepting public input."
- Once you are on the document page, select the "Next Edition" tab.
- Choose the link "The next edition of this standard is now open for Public Input." You will be asked to sign in or create a free online account with NFPA before using this system.
- Follow the online instructions to submit your Public Input (see www.nfpa.org/publicinput for detailed instructions).
- Once a Public Input is saved or submitted in the system, it can be located on the "My Profile" page by selecting the "My Public Inputs/Comments/NITMAMs" section.

Submit a Public Comment

Once the First Draft Report becomes available there is a Public Comment period. Any objections or further related changes to the content of the First Draft must be submitted at the Comment Stage. To submit a Public Comment follow the same steps as previously explained for the submission of Public Input.

Other Resources Available on the Document Information Pages

Header: View document title and scope, access to our codes and standards or NFCSS subscription, and sign up to receive email alerts.

Current & Prior Editions	Research current and previous edition information.
Next Edition	Follow the committee's progress in the processing of a standard in its next revision cycle.
Technical Committee	View current committee rosters or apply to a committee.
Ask a Technical Question	For members, officials, and AHJs to submit standards questions to NFPA staff. Our Technical Questions Service provides a convenient way to receive timely and consistent technical assistance when you need to know more about NFPA standards relevant to your work.
News	Provides links to available articles and research and statistical reports related to our standards.
Purchase Products & Training	Discover and purchase the latest products and training.
Related Products	View related publications, training, and other resources available for purchase.

Information on the NFPA Standards Development Process

I. Applicable Regulations. The primary rules governing the processing of NFPA standards (codes, standards, recommended practices, and guides) are the NFPA *Regulations Governing the Development of NFPA Standards (Regs)*. Other applicable rules include NFPA *Bylaws*, NFPA *Technical Meeting Convention Rules*, NFPA *Guide for the Conduct of Participants in the NFPA Standards Development Process*, and the NFPA *Regulations Governing Petitions to the Board of Directors from Decisions of the Standards Council*. Most of these rules and regulations are contained in the *NFPA Standards Directory*. For copies of the *Directory*, contact Codes and Standards Administration at NFPA headquarters; all these documents are also available on the NFPA website at "www.nfpa.org/regs."

The following is general information on the NFPA process. All participants, however, should refer to the actual rules and regulations for a full understanding of this process and for the criteria that govern participation.

II. Technical Committee Report. The Technical Committee Report is defined as "the Report of the responsible Committee(s), in accordance with the Regulations, in preparation of a new or revised NFPA Standard." The Technical Committee Report is in two parts and consists of the First Draft Report and the Second Draft Report. (See *Regs* at Section 1.4.)

III. Step 1: First Draft Report. The First Draft Report is defined as "Part one of the Technical Committee Report, which documents the Input Stage." The First Draft Report consists of the First Draft, Public Input, Committee Input, Committee and Correlating Committee Statements, Correlating Notes, and Ballot Statements. (See *Regs* at 4.2.5.2 and Section 4.3.) Any objection to an action in the First Draft Report must be raised through the filing of an appropriate Comment for consideration in the Second Draft Report or the objection will be considered resolved. [See *Regs* at 4.3.1(b).]

IV. Step 2: Second Draft Report. The Second Draft Report is defined as "Part two of the Technical Committee Report, which documents the Comment Stage." The Second Draft Report consists of the Second Draft, Public Comments with corresponding Committee Actions and Committee Statements, Correlating Notes and their respective Committee Statements, Committee Comments, Correlating Revisions, and Ballot Statements. (See *Regs* at 4.2.5.2 and Section 4.4.) The First Draft Report and the Second Draft Report together constitute the Technical Committee Report. Any outstanding objection following the Second Draft Report must be raised through an appropriate Amending Motion at the NFPA Technical Meeting or the objection will be considered resolved. [See *Regs* at 4.4.1(b).]

V. Step 3a: Action at NFPA Technical Meeting. Following the publication of the Second Draft Report, there is a period during which those wishing to make proper Amending Motions on the Technical Committee Reports must signal their intention by submitting a Notice of Intent to Make a Motion (NITMAM). (See *Regs* at 4.5.2.) Standards that receive notice of proper Amending Motions (Certified Amending Motions) will be presented for action at the annual June NFPA Technical Meeting. At the meeting, the NFPA membership can consider and act on these Certified Amending Motions as well as Follow-up Amending Motions, that is, motions that become necessary as a result of a previous successful Amending Motion. (See 4.5.3.2 through 4.5.3.6 and Table 1, Columns 1-3 of *Regs* for a summary of the available Amending Motions and who may make them.) Any outstanding objection following action at an NFPA Technical Meeting (and any further Technical Committee consideration following successful Amending Motions, see *Regs* at 4.5.3.7 through 4.6.5) must be raised through an appeal to the Standards Council or it will be considered to be resolved.

VI. Step 3b: Documents Forwarded Directly to the Council. Where no NITMAM is received and certified in accordance with the *Technical Meeting Convention Rules*, the standard is forwarded directly to the Standards Council for action on issuance. Objections are deemed to be resolved for these documents. (See *Regs* at 4.5.2.5.)

VII. Step 4a: Council Appeals. Anyone can appeal to the Standards Council concerning procedural or substantive matters related to the development, content, or issuance of any document of the NFPA or on matters within the purview of the authority of the Council, as established by the *Bylaws* and as determined by the Board of Directors. Such appeals must be in written form and filed with the Secretary of the Standards Council (see *Regs* at Section 1.6). Time constraints for filing an appeal must be in accordance with 1.6.2 of the *Regs*. Objections are deemed to be resolved if not pursued at this level.

VIII. Step 4b: Document Issuance. The Standards Council is the issuer of all documents (see Article 8 of *Bylaws*). The Council acts on the issuance of a document presented for action at an NFPA Technical Meeting within 75 days from the date of the recommendation from the NFPA Technical Meeting, unless this period is extended by the Council (see *Regs* at 4.7.2). For documents forwarded directly to the Standards Council, the Council acts on the issuance of the document at its next scheduled meeting, or at such other meeting as the Council may determine (see *Regs* at 4.5.2.5 and 4.7.4).

IX. Petitions to the Board of Directors. The Standards Council has been delegated the responsibility for the administration of the codes and standards development process and the issuance of documents. However, where extraordinary circumstances requiring the intervention of the Board of Directors exist, the Board of Directors may take any action necessary to fulfill its obligations to preserve the integrity of the codes and standards development process and to protect the interests of the NFPA. The rules for petitioning the Board of Directors can be found in the *Regulations Governing Petitions to the Board of Directors from Decisions of the Standards Council* and in Section 1.7 of the *Regs*.

X. For More Information. The program for the NFPA Technical Meeting (as well as the NFPA website as information becomes available) should be consulted for the date on which each report scheduled for consideration at the meeting will be presented. To view the First Draft Report and Second Draft Report as well as information on NFPA rules and for up-to-date information on schedules and deadlines for processing NFPA documents, check the NFPA website (www.nfpa.org/docinfo) or contact NFPA Codes & Standards Administration at (617) 984-7246.

TRAINING DESIGNED AROUND THE WORK YOU DO.

Get safety training directly from NFPA.

When you're responsible at the highest level for safety on the job site or ensuring that safety equipment is installed properly, it's important to be knowledgeable about the latest technologies. NFPA® training can provide you with a valuable opportunity to gain experience with the very systems you'll work with on the job.

ONLINE | ON-SITE | CLASSROOM | Learn more at **nfpa.org/training**